COLLECTIONS

Practice Book

GRADE 4

Harcourt

Orlando   Boston   Dallas   Chicago   San Diego

Visit *The Learning Site!*
www.harcourtschool.com

Contents

TOUCH A DREAM

ISBN 0-15-312714-7

09 10 11 12 13 054 2009 2008 2007 2006 2005 2004

Name _____

My Name Is
María Isabel

Grammar:
Imperative and
Exclamatory
Sentences

▶ **Label each sentence** *imperative* **or** *exclamatory*.

1. Wow, this song is difficult!   _____

2. Please play it one more time.   _____

3. What a nice tune it has!   _____

4. Listen to the low part.   _____

5. How lovely it sounds!   _____

▶ **Rewrite these sentences. Add the correct end marks.**

6. Sing the Hanukkah song again _____

_____

7. Tell us the story of Hanukkah _____

_____

8. What an interesting story it is _____

_____

9. Light the candles carefully _____

_____

10. How pretty they look _____

_____

 TRY THIS! Write a paragraph about a holiday you love. Use all four kinds of sentences (declarative, interrogative, imperative, exclamatory).

Harcourt

Name _____

▶ **Write a Spelling Word to complete each sentence.**

1. Before we go to _____ Grandma, we'll
   buy you some new shoes.

2. Let's _____ to the shoe store.

3. We'll check to see if you need a

   larger _____ now.

4. Which _____ of shoe do you
   like—casual or dressy?

5. Do you want shoes that slip on or shoes that

   _____?

6. I can tell by your

   _____

   that those are the
   shoes you want.

SPELLING WORDS
1. mine
2. tie
3. wild
4. type
5. smile
6. drive
7. size
8. blind
9. visit
10. thick
11. die
12. prize

▶ **Write the Spelling Word that rhymes with each word below.**

7. stick _____   10. tries _____

8. nine _____   11. child _____

9. sigh _____   12. kind _____

Handwriting Tip: Be careful not to loop the letter *i*.
Otherwise, it might look like an *e*. Write the Spelling Words
below.

13. smile _____   15. tie _____

14. visit _____   16. prize _____

Harcourt

▶ **Write the word from the box that matches each definition.
Two words will be used twice.**

immigrants	salary	modest	valuable
appreciation	courageous	tremendous	sportsmanship

1. thankfulness
2. very large or great

2. t r e M e n d o v g (down)
1. _____ (across)

5. not boastful
6. brave

6. c e u r a g e o u s (down)
5. _____ (across)

3. people who come from
   another country
4. behavior in a game

4. S p o r t s m a n s h i p (down)
3. _____ (across)

7. gratefulness
8. money earned

8. s a l a r y (down)
7. s a l a r y (across)

9. money paid
   for work
10. worth a lot

10. V a l u a b l e (down)
9. _____ (across)

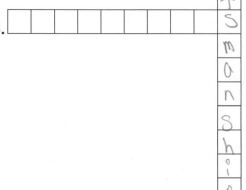

SCHOOL-HOME CONNECTION With your child, talk about people in
sports, politics, or entertainment whom you admire. Write a list of the
reasons you like each one. Use at least three Vocabulary Words.

Harcourt

Touch a Dream **23**

Name _____

| **Skill Reminder** | prefix + base word = new word |
| | base word + suffix = new word |

▶ Read the news article and write the word that best fits each definition in parentheses. Choose from the words in the box and add the correct prefix or suffix.

Prefix:	dis- pre- in- im-
Suffix:	-al -ful -ly -ous -less -ty
Words:	capable help possible quick courage
	pleased arranged loyal nation hand

NEW YORK, New York. October 20, 1957—Now that the 1957 season has ended, it is **(1) (not possible)**

_____ to find more than one major league baseball team whose home is New York City. For years the Yankees, Dodgers, and Giants have fought for the **(2) (quality of being loyal)** _____ of New York fans. Now only the Yankees will remain. Many baseball fans are **(3) (not capable)**

_____ of understanding why the Giants and Dodgers have moved to California. To a **(4) (amount that fills a hand)**

_____ of New York fans, this is a **(5) (having courage)**

_____ step to give baseball lovers in the West a chance to watch the **(6) (having to do with the nation)** _____ pastime. However, many others are **(7) (the opposite of pleased)**

_____ with the owners' decision to take their much-loved teams away, but they are **(8) (lacking help)**

_____ to do anything about it. Fans in Los Angeles and San Francisco have **(9) (arranged in advance)** _____ celebrations to welcome their new teams, and officials are sure that baseball will **(10) (in a quick way)**

_____ become even more popular in California.

Harcourt

▶ **Fill in the first two columns of the K-W-L chart. Then use information from the story to fill in the last column.**

K What I Know	**W** What I Want to Know	**L** What I Learned

▶ **List five reasons why Lou Gehrig was admired both as a player and as a person by so many fans.**

1. _____

2. _____

3. _____

4. _____

5. _____

Harcourt

Name _____

▶ **Write the word identification strategy you used from the list in the box to figure out the meaning of each underlined word in the paragraph.**

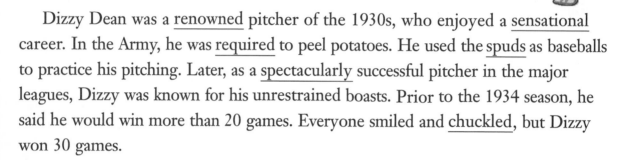

- Think about the sounds the letters represent.
- Look for familiar word parts or for shorter words inside a longer word.
- Look for familiar patterns of letters in parts of the word.

- Blend sounds at the beginning of the word with vowel patterns.
- Look for spelling patterns.
- See if other words give clues about the word's meaning.

Dizzy Dean was a <u>renowned</u> pitcher of the 1930s, who enjoyed a <u>sensational</u> career. In the Army, he was <u>required</u> to peel potatoes. He used the <u>spuds</u> as baseballs to practice his pitching. Later, as a <u>spectacularly</u> successful pitcher in the major leagues, Dizzy was known for his unrestrained boasts. Prior to the 1934 season, he said he would win more than 20 games. Everyone smiled and <u>chuckled</u>, but Dizzy won 30 games.

1. renowned _____

2. sensational _____

_____

3. required _____

4. spuds _____

_____

5. spectacularly _____

6. chuckled _____

SCHOOL-HOME CONNECTION With your child, start a list of interesting or unfamiliar words that you find in print. Ask your child to tell how he or she figures out how to pronounce or figure out the meanings of new words.

Harcourt

Name _____

▶ **Write a compound word by using two of the three words given. An example has been done for you.**

Example:

basket	team	ball	basketball

1. team   base   mate   _teammate_

2. race   ball   track   _racetrack_

3. field   out   base   _out feild_

4. keeper   team   goal   _goal keeper_

5. base   track   ball   _baseball_

6. foot   basket   race   _footrace_

7. board   basket   score   _scoreboard_

8. trap   park   ball   _ball park_

9. play   hit   base   _hit base_

10. ball   high   fly   _fly ball_

11. play   game   double   _play game_

12. field   run   home   ~~home~~ _homerun_

Write down all the sport terms you can think of that are compound words, such as *racquetball* and *tennis ball*. Use a dictionary if necessary.

Harcourt

▶ **Draw one line under each subject. Draw two lines under each predicate.**

1. I visited the Baseball Hall of Fame.

2. The museum has pictures of Lou Gehrig.

3. Some pictures show Babe Ruth, too.

4. Cooperstown is a wonderful place.

5. Many schoolchildren travel to the museum.

▶ **Add a subject or a predicate to complete each sentence.**

6. This baseball team _____.

7. _____ caught the ball.

8. _____ threw it to second base.

9. The runner _____.

10. _____ cheered in the stands.

 TRY THIS! Write five sentences about a sport you like. Draw one line under the subject and two lines under the predicate in each sentence you write.

Name _____

▶ **Use the Spelling Words and the clues below to complete the puzzle.**

Across

1. the person who helps team players
2. the month after May
3. opposite of *minus*
4. music
5. firm
6. knocked into pieces

Down

7. opposite of *sinking*
8. not these, but _____
9. a group of workers on a ship
10. disturbed
11. perform surgery
12. opposite of *leave out*

SPELLING WORDS

1. *those*
2. *coach*
3. *solid*
4. *include*
5. *crew*
6. *plus*
7. *operate*
8. *broke*
9. *upset*
10. *tune*
11. *June*
12. *floating*

Handwriting Tip: Make sure your letters sit evenly on the lower writing line. Write the Spelling Words below.

coach

13. tune ___tune___   15. upset ___upset___

14. June ___June___   16. plus ___plus___

SCHOOL-HOME CONNECTION With your child, think of words that are related to baseball that have long or short *o* or *u* in them, such as *home run*.

Harcourt

Name _____

▶ **Write the word from the box that matches each definition.**

| earnestly | blizzard | frantically | stagger | scoured | bustled |

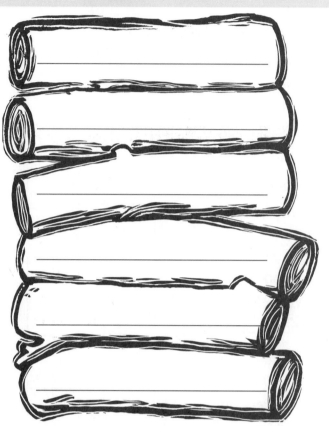

1. in a wild and excited way   _____

2. hurried busily   _____

3. a snowstorm   _____

4. in a serious way   _____

5. to walk in an unsteady way   _____

6. rubbed and scraped   _____

▶ **Write a word from the box to complete each sentence.**

Once the girls realized that the **(7)** _____ had

snowed them in, they tried **(8)** _____ to get the

door open. When that didn't work, they **(9)** _____
about to find tools they might be able to use. They noticed the

storm had **(10)** _____ the windowpane and
the glass looked cracked. Then they phoned for help and believed

(11) _____ that they would be rescued. After some

time, they saw someone carrying a shovel **(12)** _____
toward the house. Help had arrived.

SCHOOL-HOME CONNECTION With your child, talk about
a situation that calls for quick-thinking action. Use at least two
Vocabulary Words.

Harcourt

Name _____

▶ **Complete the cause-and-effect fishbone.**

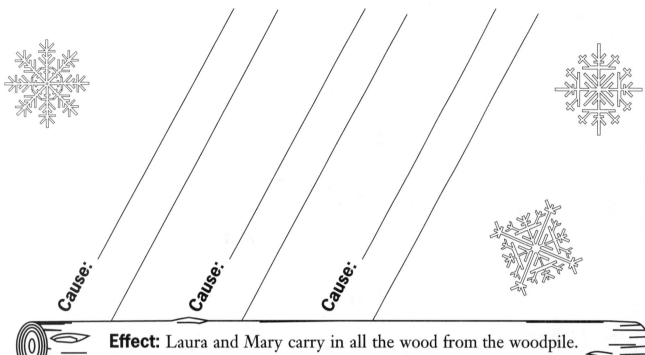

Cause:

Cause:

Cause:

Effect: Laura and Mary carry in all the wood from the woodpile.

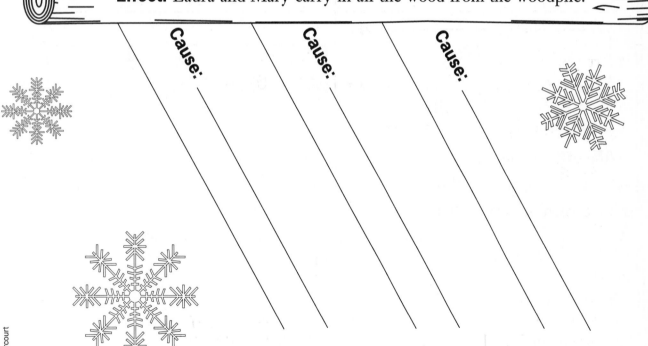

Cause:

Cause:

Cause:

▶ **What does the girls' experience teach them and their parents?**

_____

_____

Name _____

▶ Below each want ad, write *first person* or *third person* to
indicate the point of view. Then write two pronouns from
the ad that helped you know.

NEEDED: STRONG PERSON to chop
wood for my fireplace. I will provide
breakfast. See Walter at the General
Store after 8:00 A.M.

1. Point of view: _____

2. Pronouns: _____

JOB OPEN NOW for patient person
to train my dog. I expect gentleness
and respect. See Mrs. Walker at the
Post Office.

5. Point of view: _____

6. Pronouns: _____

WANTED! Teacher for one-room
school. Townspeople will pay well
for a good teacher for their children.
They offer free room and board.
See Mayor Robinson.

3. Point of view: _____

4. Pronouns: _____

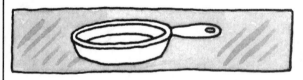

GOOD COOK NEEDED NOW for
single homesteader. He is hungry for
home cooking! Work in his kitchen
for a good salary. See Henry one
mile south of town.

7. Point of view: _____

8. Pronouns: _____

HIRED HAND needed for our farm.
We need help planting crops.
See Mr. Fuller any time.

9. Point of view: _____

10. Pronouns: _____

Harcourt

Name _____

▶ **Rewrite each want ad from page 32. Use the other point of
view. For example, if the ad was written in the first-person
point of view, rewrite it in the third-person point of view.**

1. **NEEDED: STRONG PERSON** _____

_____

_____

_____

_____

3. **JOB OPEN NOW** _____

_____

_____

_____

_____

2. **WANTED!** _____

_____

_____

_____

_____

_____

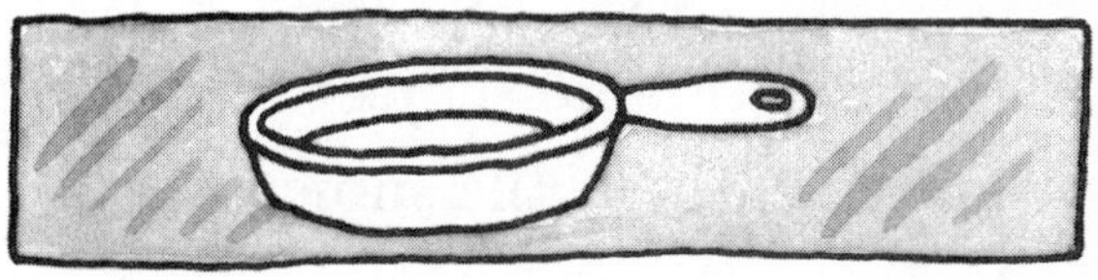

4. **GOOD COOK NEEDED NOW** _____

_____

_____

_____

_____

5. **HIRED HAND** _____

_____

Touch a Dream   **33**

Name _____

▶ **Draw one line under each complete subject. Then circle
each simple subject.**

1. Little Laura swept the floor.

2. Her sister cleared the table.

3. The two girls washed the dishes.

4. Their house seemed very quiet.

5. Every chore was finished.

▶ **Add a complete subject to complete each sentence.
Circle each simple subject.**

6. _____ set the table.

7. _____ lay on the tablecloth.

8. _____ came out of the oven.

9. _____ smelled delicious.

10. _____ tasted wonderful.

11. _____ sat down.

12. _____ passed the bread.

TRY THIS! Write five sentences about doing household chores. Circle the simple
subject of each sentence.

Harcourt

Name _____

► **The letters of the underlined words are mixed up. Write the correct Spelling Words on the lines.**

1. One <u>nnftarooe</u>, Pa and I went walking

in the woods. _afternoon_

2. I saw a <u>unddwoe</u> squirrel. _wounded_

3. "Who would <u>ohost</u> such a cute animal?" I

wondered. _shoot_

4. Its fur is <u>oomsht</u> and shiny. _smooth_

5. "I'll <u>sobot</u> myself up so I can see," Pa said.

boost

6. The squirrel is <u>ingloof</u> us! _fooling_

7. That put me in a good <u>omdo</u>. _mood_

SPELLING WORDS
1. hoop
2. wounded
3. shoot
4. booth
5. broom
6. boost
7. mood
8. fooling
9. afternoon
10. spoon
11. smooth
12. tooth

► **Write the Spelling Word that names each picture.**

8. _spoon_   **11.** _broom_

9. _tooth_   **12.** _hoop_

10. _booth_

Handwriting Tip: Make sure your letters are not too light or too dark. Make them smooth and even. Write the Spelling Words below.

spoon

13. shoot _____   **15.** smooth _____

14. boost _____   **16.** fooling _____

SCHOOL-HOME CONNECTION With your child, think of words that sound like *boot*. Then try to use as many of these words as you can in a short story.

Touch a Dream **35**

Harcourt

▶ **Finish each sentence with a word from the box. Use each word twice.**

| anticipation | unfamiliar | thicket | clearing | unity |

1. I love hiking, dad. I'm bursting with

_____!

2. The trees are so close together in this

_____.

I hope we don't get lost.

3. I'm _____ with this part of the woods.

4. Family, let's stay together. Remember the importance of

_____.

5. We'll have to help each other find a way through the

_____

of trees.

6. I see a

_____

where some trees have been cut down.

7. I brought food for lunch and an umbrella in

_____ of rain.

8. We should check the map. This area looks _____ to me.

9. When we get into the open

_____,

let's stop to eat and check our directions.

10. We'll work together. With

_____, I

know we'll be okay.

 TRY THIS! Write a set of directions for someone hiking in the woods. Use at least two Vocabulary Words.

Harcourt

Name _____

▶ Complete the Venn diagram below by telling how the seven
children behave at the beginning and at the end of the story.
Then write ways the children behave that stay the same through
the whole story.

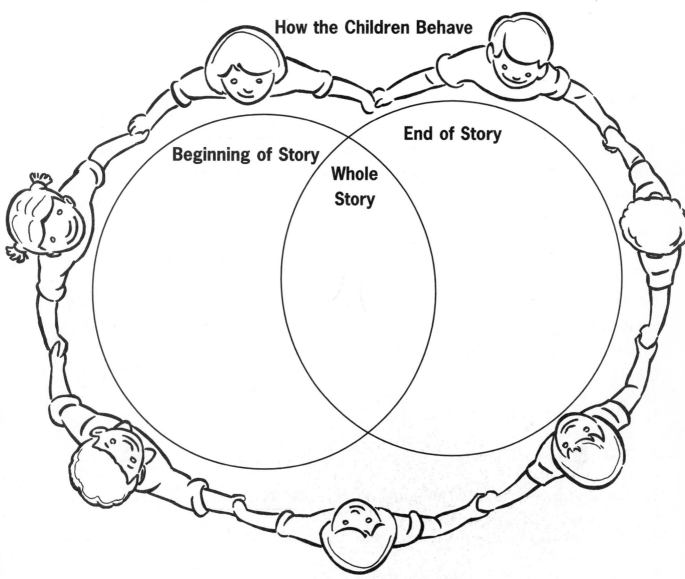

How the Children Behave

Beginning of Story

End of Story

**Whole
Story**

▶ Briefly describe how the children learn the value of unity.

_____

_____

_____

_____

_____

Name _____

▶ **Read the title and each part of the story. Then use story clues and what you already know to answer each question.**

The Three Foolish Woodsmen and the Donkey: A Fable

Once upon a time there were three men who worked in the forest. They gathered fallen logs and cut them into firewood. "Let's take our wood into the village to sell," said the first man. "We can each carry some," said the second. "No, only you two can carry the wood," said the third man. "I must lead our donkey."

"You are right," said the other two men, as each took a huge load of wood into his arms and began to walk down the long path. The third man led the donkey.

"We must stop and rest," panted the first woodsman.

"Yes," agreed the second, dropping his load of wood.

"I am not tired at all," said the third. "We must hurry on to the village so we can sell our wood before the sun goes down." The men began to argue. The donkey brayed and pawed the ground. Suddenly an old woman appeared beside them on the path.

"All three of you are silly," she said. "There's no need to argue. I can tell you what to do to solve your problem."

1. Is the story fiction or nonfiction? _____

2. What makes you think that? _____

3. How do the two men who are carrying the wood feel? _____

4. What makes you think that? _____

5. How do you think the third man feels? _____

6. What do you think the woman will tell the men to do to solve their problem?

_____

7. What makes you think that? _____

8. Do you think the men will follow the old woman's advice? Why?

_____

Harcourt

Name _____

▶ Read each story. Then read each question and choose the best answer. Mark the letter for that answer.

Kami and her cousins wanted to feed the birds that lived in Kami's backyard. "We have some birdseed and pine cones," Kami said. "If we can make the seeds stick to the pine cones, we can hang them in the tree. Then the birds can get to them." Two-year-old Tommy looked up from his snack. His fingers were covered with peanut butter.

"I have an idea!" Kami cried.

1 The children will probably _____.

Ⓐ eat some peanut butter

Ⓑ scatter the seeds on the ground

Ⓒ use peanut butter to make the seeds stick

Ⓓ ask Tommy to make the bird feeders

2 Which will they probably *not* do?

Ⓕ make bird feeders

Ⓖ use the pine cones and peanut butter

Ⓗ throw away the peanut butter

Ⓙ find a way to feed the birds

3 The leader will probably be _____.

Ⓐ Tommy

Ⓑ one of Kami's cousins

Ⓒ a friend

Ⓓ Kami

After a while the children were hungry. Kami said they were out of peanut butter, but she saw some bread and cheese in the house.

4 The children will probably _____.

Ⓕ buy more peanut butter

Ⓖ eat nothing

Ⓗ make cheese sandwiches

Ⓙ wait until evening to eat

The next day Kami's dad hung bird feeders in the tree. Then he called Kami to the window.

5 Kami will probably see _____.

Ⓐ some birds in the tree

Ⓑ no birds at all

Ⓒ the bird feeders on the ground

Ⓓ cheese sandwiches

6 Which will the birds probably *not* do?

Ⓕ enjoy the new bird feeders

Ⓖ fly away without eating

Ⓗ come back often to the tree

Ⓙ eat the birdseed

Harcourt

Name _____

▶ **Read the story below. For each underlined word, write the homophone that fits the sentence. (Homophones are words that sound alike but have different meanings and spellings.)**

Today I **(1)** <u>herd</u> the most amazing **(2)** <u>tail</u>. It was about a young girl who lived by the ocean. She loved to fish. Each day, when the **(3)** <u>tied</u> came in, she dropped her nets in the water.

Late one **(4)** <u>knight</u> she pulled out a very large fish. She was happy because she knew she could sell it and **(5)** <u>by</u> a new comb for her **(6)** <u>hare</u>. Then the fish started to talk.

"Where are you taking me?" asked the fish. The girl didn't know what to say. Then the fish said, "Can we wait for a while? It is only one more **(7)** <u>our</u> until **(8)** <u>mourning</u>, and I want to see the sun rise one more time. Then I will go with you to the market."

What could the girl do? She put the fish in a bucket of water and sat down to **(9)** <u>weight</u> for the sunrise. Soon she fell asleep. Do you **(10)** <u>no</u> what happened? When she woke up, the tide had gone out. The fish was nowhere to **(11)** <u>bee</u> found. It was far, far **(12)** <u>aweigh</u>.

1. _____   5. _____   9. _____

2. _____   6. _____   10. _____

3. _____   7. _____   11. _____

4. _____   8. _____   12. _____

 TRY THIS! Think of three pairs of homophones different from the ones shown above. Then use each one in a sentence.

Harcourt

▶ **Draw two lines under the complete predicate. Then circle the simple predicate.**

1. The oldest child found two flint stones.

2. One child unfolded a large quilt.

3. The youngest child screamed in terror.

4. The others ran to his side.

5. All of the children shared their stories.

▶ **Add a complete predicate to each subject. Circle the simple predicate in each complete predicate you write.**

6. The campfire _____.

7. Water from the canteen _____.

8. Banana bread _____.

9. The map _____.

10. All seven children _____.

11. Their father _____.

12. The family _____.

TRY THIS! Write four sentences giving examples of people helping each other. Circle the simple predicate in each sentence you write.

Harcourt

Name _____

▶ **Write a Spelling Word to complete each sentence. Use the picture clues.**

1. It _____ all night long.

2. Its _____ will wake you up.

3. A turkey needs to be

   _____ .

4. Get set to _____!

5. We _____ in the garage.

▶ **Write the Spelling Word that fits each clue.**

6. opposite of *softer*   _____

7. at a greater distance   _____

8. a diagram   _____

9. cleverest   _____

10. hurt   _____

11. suffered from hunger   _____

12. seeds and flowers   _____

Handwriting Tip: Close the letter *a* at the top. Do not loop the downstroke, or the *a* could look like *cl*. Write the Spelling Words below.

13. carved _____   15. alarm _____

14. barked _____   16. harder _____

SCHOOL-HOME CONNECTION With your child, think of other words with the /är/sound. Then use them in a story.

▶ **Read the words on the flowers. Then write the word that
answers each riddle. Use each word twice.**

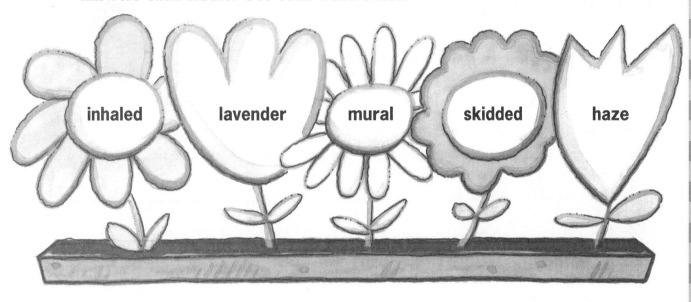

inhaled lavender mural skidded haze

1. I am a shade of purple.
   What color am I? _____

2. I was running fast. When I stopped
   quickly, I slid. What did I do? _____

3. I did this when I took air into my body.
   What did I do? _____

4. I can make it hard to see.
   What am I? _____

5. I am a very large picture made by
   one or more artists. What am I? _____

6. I am like a fog.
   What am I? _____

7. I'm a plant as well as a color.
   What am I? _____

8. I mean "breathed in."
   What word am I? _____

9. I am art that is painted on a wall.
   What am I? _____

10. When I stopped my bike, I left tire
    marks on the road. What did I do? _____

SCHOOL-HOME CONNECTION With your child, make up riddles
about items in your home. Use some Vocabulary Words in your
riddles. For example, "I smell like lavender. You put me on your
skin. What am I?" Guess the answers to each other's riddles.

Harcourt

Name _____

Skill Reminder | your knowledge and experience + story clues = your prediction

▶ **Read each story part. Then complete each sentence.**

"That blank brick wall on the back of our school isn't very pretty," Mr. Bromley said. "I wonder if there's anything we can do about it."

"Our art class has been looking for a project to do this year," said Luis.

1. The art class will probably _____.

2. That is my prediction because _____

_____.

On Wednesday, Luis said, "Tomorrow and Friday are school holidays for spring break. Let's start painting tomorrow."

"I'm busy tomorrow," said Alicia. "How about waiting until Friday to paint?"

"I heard something about rain that day," said Mr. Bromley.

3. The class will probably start painting on _____.

4. That is my prediction because _____

_____.

The students worked hard all day and finished their painting.

"Let's plan a picnic for Saturday to celebrate," Mr. Bromley said.

"That's a great idea," agreed Luis. "Should we have the picnic in the morning or in the afternoon?"

5. The students will probably plan to have their picnic in the _____.

6. That is my prediction because _____

_____.

TRY THIS! What do you predict the students will do if it rains on Saturday afternoon?

Harcourt

Name _____

▶ As you read, start to fill in the prediction web. After you read, write what actually happens.

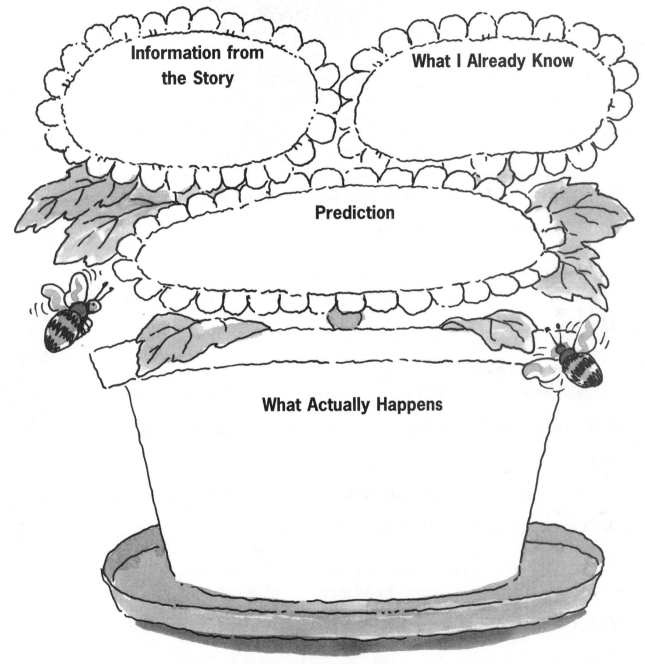

Information from the Story

What I Already Know

Prediction

What Actually Happens

▶ Describe Marisol's problems and solutions.

_____

_____

_____

_____

Harcourt

Name _____

▶ **Read each example of figurative language. Then write what each sentence means from the choices given.**

1. Mrs. Garza's flower garden was like a box of crayons.

The garden was _____.
very colorful   **made of wax**   **square-shaped**

2. Mr. Potter's cornstalks marched from one end of the garden to the other.

The cornstalks _____.
walked   **were in a parade**   **stood in long rows**

3. Larissa's face was one big question mark.

Larissa's face _____.
was sad   **was pear-shaped**   **showed she was puzzled**

4. Her tomato plants were flinging green arms everywhere.

Her tomato plants _____.
were green   **had sprouted arms**   **were growing everywhere**

5. Larissa put on her thinking cap and figured out what was wrong.

Larissa _____.
wore a hat   **thought hard**   **designed a cap**

6. "I need to give those plants a hand," she said.

She needed to _____.
help the plants   **water the plants**   **clap for the plants**

7. Larissa put a wire cage around each plant, so it could touch the sky.

She helped each plant _____.
grow branches   **grow tall**   **grow into the clouds**

8. "Our gardens are our grocery stores," Mrs. Garza said.

The gardens _____.
are marketplaces   **provide food**   **grow inside stores**

SCHOOL-HOME CONNECTION With your child, listen for examples of figurative language you hear in everyday speech, on television, and on the radio. Start a list. Work with your child to write the real meaning next to each phrase.

Harcourt

Name _____

▶ Draw one line under each simple subject.
Draw two lines under each simple predicate.
Label each sentence *compound subject* or *compound predicate*.

1. Marisol and her friends worked. _____

2. They weeded and hoed. _____

3. The garden blossomed and grew. _____

4. That man or his wife watered the plants.

_____

5. He, she, and I picked beans. _____

6. The hose twists, turns, and sprays the plants.

_____

▶ Rewrite these sentences. Add commas where they are needed.

7. The beans tomatoes and greens are ready to pick. _____

_____

8. Teenagers children and their parents watch. _____

_____

9. We sprinkle soak or splash the vegetables. _____

_____

10. Did Marisol Mr. Ortiz or Mr. Singh see the butterfly? _____

_____

TRY THIS! Write two sentences about gardening. Write one sentence with a compound subject and one with a compound predicate.

Harcourt

Name _____

▶ **Read this newspaper article. Find and circle the twelve misspelled words. Then write each word correctly on the lines below.**

Three murals went on display today at Day School. Students worked in groups to plan and paint them.

One mural's theme is *space*. Against a deep blue background, planets orbet the sun. Light seems to poar from the sun, our sourse of light and heat here on Earth.

Another group chose *spourts* for its mural's theme. A player throws a basketball fourward toward the hoop to scoar. A teammate, sidelined with a soir knee, cheers. The team has on uniforms players woer years ago.

The third mural's theme is *work* and shows how people suport themselves. It shows workers using machines to forse huge rocks out of the way. Other people bring oardar to a littered street.

Please, go and see the murals for yurself.

SPELLING WORDS
1. pour
2. orbit
3. score
4. source
5. sports
6. forward
7. force
8. order
9. wore
10. yourself
11. support
12. sore

1. _____   7. _____

2. _____   8. _____

3. _____   9. _____

4. _____   10. _____

5. _____   11. _____

6. _____   12. _____

Handwriting Tip: When you write the *r* in the letter combination *or*, be careful to curve up and slant down. Otherwise, the letters *or* might look like *oi*. Write the Spelling Words below.

13. orbit _____   15. order _____

14. sports _____   16. support _____

Harcourt

venture **uninhabited** **burrows** **stranded** **nestles** **instinctively**

▶ **Write the word from above that matches each definition.**

1. left alone _____

2. by nature _____

3. to travel at some risk _____

4. snuggles _____

5. not lived in by anyone _____

6. holes dug in the ground _____

▶ **Write the Vocabulary Word that best completes each sentence.**

Rabbits live in **(7)** _____ they dig in the ground.

Sometimes other creatures **(8)** _____ inside these holes,

not knowing whether they are already occupied or **(9)** _____.
One time my brother stepped in one of these holes and couldn't get his foot out.

He was **(10)** _____ until my father found him and got him
out. My brother is afraid of getting stuck again, so wherever he walks in our yard,

he now **(11)** _____ watches for holes. We know that in our

yard, a rabbit family **(12)** _____ beneath our feet.

TRY THIS! Imagine you are a puffling trying to fly for the first time. Write sentences that tell what it feels like. Use at least two Vocabulary Words.

Harcourt

Name _____

Skill Reminder Use sounds, letter patterns, spelling patterns, and context clues to help you figure out new words.

▶ Write the strategy you used from the list below to figure out the meaning of each underlined word.

- **Think about the sounds the letters represent.**
- **Look for familiar word parts or shorter words inside a longer word.**
- **Look for familiar patterns of letters in parts of the word.**
- **Look for spelling patterns.**
- **See if other words give clues about the word's meaning.**

1. <u>Geothermal</u> energy under the earth's surface is used to heat homes in

   Iceland. _____

2. This is heat that is <u>generated</u> inside the earth. _____

   _____

3. Sometimes <u>magma</u>, or melted rock, lies near the surface of the earth. _____

   _____

4. Rocks around the magma heat the <u>groundwater</u>. _____

   _____

5. In Iceland the heated water is <u>transported</u> to homes through pipes. _____

   _____

6. Iceland is known for its <u>geysers</u>, which are hot springs where steam and

   water shoot up. _____

7. Old Faithful erupts on <u>schedule</u> about every 50 to 100 minutes. _____

   _____

Harcourt

Name _____

▶ Fill in the first two columns of the K-W-L chart. Then use information from the story to fill in the third column.

K	W	L
What I Know	**What I Want to Know**	**What I Learned**

▶ Write a one-sentence summary of the whole selection.

_____

_____

Name _____

▶ **Read the story. Then write the correct causes and effects to complete the chart.**

"Cheep! Tweet!" It was only a tiny sound, but it caused Patrick to stop his bike and look under the bush. There he found a little bird. It tried to fly away when it saw Patrick, but one of its wings was injured. Since Patrick didn't know what to do to help the bird, he dashed up the sidewalk and rang the doorbell at Mr. Grant's house.

"Mr. Grant, can you help? You know a lot about birds, and I've found one that has a hurt wing," Patrick said. Mr. Grant got gloves, a small box with air holes and a cover, and a small towel, and he followed Patrick to the bush. He carefully picked up the injured bird and put it into the box.

"You were right to call me," Mr. Grant said. "People shouldn't try to care for wild creatures at home, so we'll take it to the Wildlife Rescue Center where I work." At the center, the manager told Patrick, "Because you were careful and gentle, this bird will soon be as strong as ever. She will fly again."

Causes	Effects
Because Patrick heard a noise,	he **(1)** _____ and **(2)** _____ .
Finding the bird caused Patrick to	**(3)** _____ and **(4)** _____ .
Because people shouldn't **(5)** _____ _____	Mr. Grant and Patrick **(6)** _____ .
Since Patrick was **(7)** _____ and **(8)** _____ with the bird,	the bird will soon be **(9)** _____ _____ and will be **(10)** _____ _____ .

Harcourt

Name _____

▶ **Read the passage. Then read each question and choose the best answer. Mark the letter for that answer.**

Hundreds of years ago huge sheets of ice called *glaciers* covered a small island called Iceland. When the big glaciers melted, lake-sized chunks of ice stayed buried in the ground. After a time, these chunks melted and left holes in the ground that eventually filled with water. That is why present-day Iceland is dotted with lakes.

Only a small part of Iceland can be used for farming, so many Icelanders make their living by fishing. Since the growing season is short, Icelanders use greenhouses to grow vegetables and fruit indoors.

Although Iceland's climate is cool, people swim outdoors in hot springs where the water is warmed.

Iceland is called the Land of Frost and Fire because it has both warm places—hot springs—and cold places—glaciers.

1 Many of Iceland's lakes were created by _____.

A hot springs

B glaciers

C rushing streams

D ponds

2 Because Iceland has so little farm land, _____.

F there is not enough to eat

G people grow their own food

H many people make their living from the sea

J people eat too much fish

3 People in Iceland use greenhouses because _____.

A the growing season is short

B they don't know much about farming

C they have large backyards

D the weather is hot

4 Because of hot springs, people in Iceland can _____.

F swim in the ocean

G swim only in the summer

H swim outdoors in cool weather

J eat more fish

5 Iceland is called the Land of Frost and Fire because it has _____.

A summer and winter seasons

B bonfires and icicles

C stoves and refrigerators

D hot springs and glaciers

Answers

1 Ⓐ Ⓑ Ⓒ Ⓓ

2 Ⓕ Ⓖ Ⓗ Ⓙ

3 Ⓐ Ⓑ Ⓒ Ⓓ

4 Ⓕ Ⓖ Ⓗ Ⓙ

5 Ⓐ Ⓑ Ⓒ Ⓓ

Harcourt

Name _____

▶ **Write the answer to each question on the line.**

1. If you wanted to find out how flamingoes care for their
   young, in which encyclopedia volume might you look? _____

2. After choosing the encyclopedia volume, what would you do? _____

   _____

3. After finding the correct article, how would you find the information you

   are looking for? _____

   _____

4. If you wanted to find the most recent list of endangered animals, would it be

   better to look in a print encyclopedia or on the Internet? _____

   _____

5. Why? _____

   _____

6. List three words separated by AND that you might use in a search for this

   information on the Internet. _____

   _____

7. After you type the search words, how do you get the computer to begin its

   search? _____

   _____

8. To find a list of endangered animals in the index of an encyclopedia, what

   entries might you look under? _____

   _____

Harcourt

Name _____

▶ **Write the key words you would use to perform a search on the Internet for the answer to each question.**

1. What birds live in a swamp?

_____ AND _____

2. What kind of nest do ospreys build?

_____ AND _____

3. What birds do you see in Texas?

_____ AND _____

4. Where is the toucan's habitat?

_____ AND _____

5. What special care does a pet parakeet need?

_____ AND _____

6. How do you train a parrot to talk?

_____ AND _____

7. What parrots are found in Africa?

_____ AND _____

8. What kinds of wildlife are found in Alaska?

_____ AND _____

9. What kind of woodpecker lives in a cactus plant?

_____ AND _____

10. Where do geese go when they migrate?

_____ AND _____

Harcourt

SCHOOL-HOME CONNECTION Talk with your child about a bird or another animal that interests both of you. Make a list of questions you would like to have answered about the creature. Together with your child, list some key words that could be used to search for the information on the Internet.

Touch a Dream **55**

Name _____

▶ **Write a word from the box to complete each analogy. An example has been done for you.**

chick	puppy	lamb	duckling
pond	pen	field	barn

Example:

Puffling is to puffin as _____cub_____ is to bear.

1. Kitten is to cat as _____ is to sheep.

2. Colt is to horse as _____ is to chicken.

3. Calf is to cow as _____ is to dog.

4. Tadpole is to frog as _____ is to duck.

5. Yard is to dog as _____ is to pig.

6. Desert is to coyote as _____ is to duck.

7. Den is to wolf as _____ is to cow.

8. Beach is to crab as _____ is to sheep.

 TRY THIS! Make a list of some of your favorite wild animals. Use a science dictionary to find out what these animals are called when they are babies. For example, a baby seal is called a pup, just like a baby dog.

Harcourt

Name _____

▶ **Identify each word group as a *comma splice* or *run-on sentence*. Then rewrite each one correctly as a compound sentence.**

1. Halla has a flashlight she carries a box. _____

_____

2. The bird fell, Halla saved it. _____

_____

▶ **Rewrite each pair of sentences as a compound sentence, using the conjunction in parentheses ( ).**

3. The birds are slow. They move well in water. **(but)**

_____

_____

4. Halla loves puffins. She helps them each year. **(and)**

_____

_____

5. Children climb the cliffs. They watch the puffins. **(and)**

_____

_____

6. The puffins ignore them. They hide in holes. **(or)**

_____

_____

Write three compound sentences about an unusual animal. Use each of the conjunctions *and, or,* and *but* once.

Harcourt

Name _____

▶ Use the Spelling Words and the clues below to complete the puzzle.

Across
5. not often
6. felt brave enough
7. having to do with milk
8. looked hard

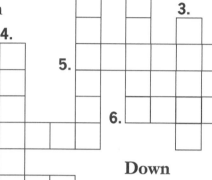

Down
1. only just
2. felt interested
3. a bright light
4. not right

SPELLING WORDS
1. cared
2. dairy
3. unfair
4. rarely
5. stared
6. dared
7. glare
8. airplanes
9. barely
10. farewell
11. software
12. staircase

▶ Put a word from the first puffin together with a word from the second puffin. Write each Spelling Word you make.

soft   fare
case   planes

stair   air
ware   well

9. _____

10. _____

11. _____

12. _____

Handwriting Tip: Be sure to bring the downstroke of *a* to the bottom writing line, or it might look like an *o*. Write the Spelling Words below.

a

13. rarely _____

14. glare _____

15. airplanes _____

16. farewell _____

Harcourt

▶ **Write the word from the web that matches each clue. Two words will be used twice.**

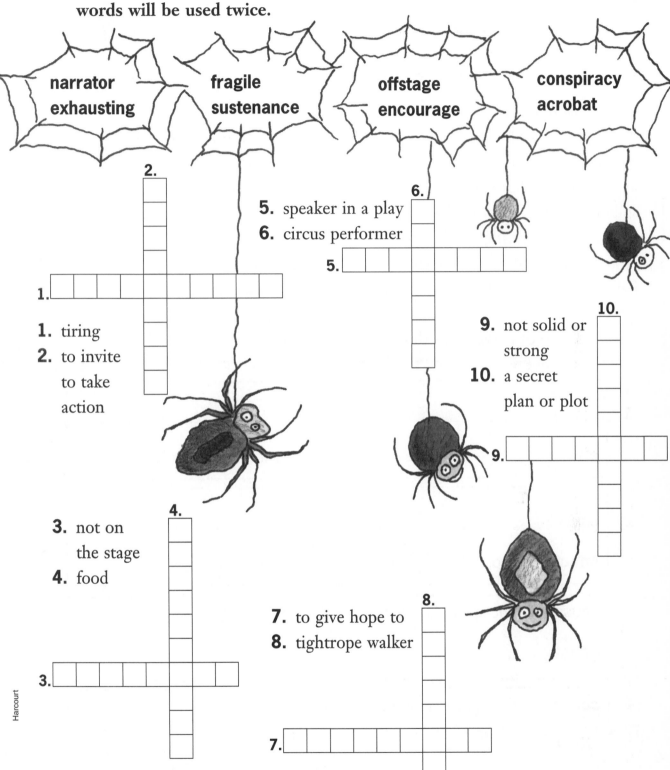

**narrator
exhausting**

**fragile
sustenance**

**offstage
encourage**

**conspiracy
acrobat**

2.

5. speaker in a play
6. circus performer

6.

5.

1.

1. tiring
2. to invite
to take
action

9. not solid or
strong
10. a secret
plan or plot

10.

9.

3. not on
the stage
4. food

4.

3.

7. to give hope to
8. tightrope walker

8.

7.

Harcourt

TRY THIS! Imagine that you are an animal on the Zuckerman farm. Describe a typical day. Use at least three Vocabulary Words.

Name _____

Skill Reminder	cause = why something happens
	effect = what happens

▶ **Read the passage. Then write four causes and their effects.**

The grass spider builds a special two-part web so it can get its food without leaving home. Here's how: the spider spins a tangle of "ropes" like a wall. Flying insects are stopped by the "ropes" and fall down. They land on a flat part of the web that the spider has woven across the branches of a bush or across a patch of grass. Since this part of the web is soft and bouncy, insects cannot move across it very well. Because the grass spider is able to zip across the web, it can reach its prey before the insect has a chance to escape. These webs are called funnel webs. Because funnel webs are thick and silky, people long ago used them as bandages.

1. **cause:** _____

   effect: The grass spider can get its food without leaving home.

2. **cause:** _____

   effect: People long ago used funnel webs as bandages.

3. **cause:** The spider is able to zip across the web.

   effect: _____

4. **cause:** The spider spins a tangle of "ropes."

   effect: _____

TRY THIS! Make a list of some causes and effects you know about insects. For example, because bees fly from flower to flower, they spread pollen.

Harcourt

Name _____

▶ Complete the story map below.

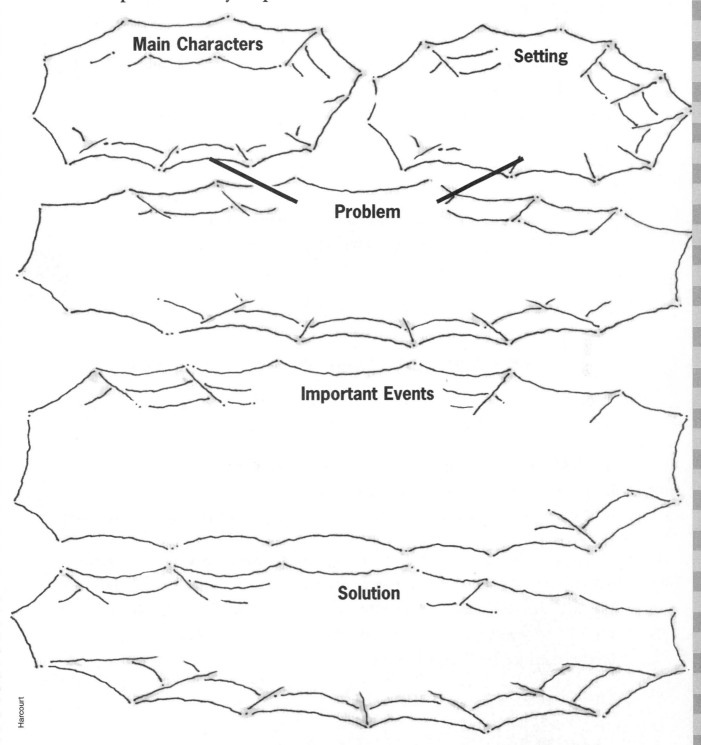

Main Characters

Setting

Problem

Important Events

Solution

Harcourt

▶ Write a one-sentence summary describing the kind of personality
Charlotte has. Base your answer on her words, thoughts, and actions.

_____

_____

Name _____

▶ **Write the theme that best fits each story summary.**

1. Joe dislikes spiders. He tries to keep them out of his vegetable garden. Then Joe learns that spiders can be helpful, because they eat harmful insects in the garden. He learns to tell the difference between harmful spiders and those that help. Joe decides that not all spiders are bad.

Theme: _____

_____

a. Don't make up your mind about a subject before you have all the facts.
b. Learn all you can about spiders before you plant a garden.
c. There are spiders that help and spiders that hurt.

2. LaShonda spends the summer on her aunt's farm. The aunt doesn't pay much attention to her niece. LaShonda helps during a storm and then gives her aunt a hug. Her aunt hugs her back and suggests that they bake cookies together.

Theme: _____

_____

a. Don't spend the summer with someone you don't know.
b. Relatives should take care of each other.
c. Some people hide their feelings and are much nicer than they seem.

3. Nathan and his older brother Lem are eight years apart in age and have very different interests. Lem mostly ignores Nathan and thinks of him as a little child. When a blizzard strikes their farm, Nathan and Lem have to work together, and Lem discovers that Nathan can do hard jobs. At the end of the story, the brothers are playing a game together.

Theme: _____

_____

a. Working together can make people appreciate each other.
b. Brothers who are far apart in age are seldom close.
c. Older brothers don't have much time for younger brothers.

Harcourt

▶ **Write the theme that best fits each story summary.**

1. Every day Lucy rides her horse from her family's homestead to the one-room school on the prairie. One day there is a huge dust storm. Lucy can see only a few inches ahead, and she has no idea which way to go. Her horse knows the way, though, and takes her safely home.

   Theme: _____

   _____

   a. Riding a horse to school can be dangerous.
   b. Animals can be good friends to people.
   c. Horses know how to navigate in the dark.

2. Sally takes care of the chickens on her family's farm. Her parents let her keep part of the money she makes from selling eggs. She saves her money and buys a fancy doll. After she buys it, fire destroys a neighbor's house. Sally thinks over an idea and then gives her new doll to the neighbor's daughter Caroline. Sally misses the doll, but she is glad to see Caroline's happy face.

   Theme: _____

   _____

   a. Giving something away can bring a special kind of happiness.
   b. You should save your money in case of emergencies.
   c. Don't save your money, because you may not keep what you buy with it.

3. When Hal visits his grandpa's farm, he is unhappy and embarrassed because he doesn't know anything about farm animals or crops. Hal is good at building and repairing things, though. When Grandpa's plow breaks, Hal is able to fix it. This makes him feel much better about himself.

   Theme: _____

   _____

   a. If you don't know something, it will be embarrassing.
   b. If you don't know about animals, learn to fix things.
   c. All kinds of talents are useful.

SCHOOL-HOME CONNECTION Discuss a story that both you and your child know. Ask your child to tell you what the story's theme is.

Touch a Dream **63**

Name _____

▶ **Beside each dictionary definition below, write a related word from the box.**

salutations	congratulations	terrific	acrobat
miracle	sustenance	supreme	magazine

1. _____ : *terrificus;* Latin for **frightened** or **excited**

2. _____ : *salutare;* Latin for **to greet** or **to welcome**

3. _____ : *acrobate;* French for **a rope dancer**

4. _____ : *soutenir;* French for **to hold up**

5. _____ : *congratulatus;* Latin for **wished joy**

6. _____ : *supremus;* Latin for **uppermost**

7. _____ : *miraculum;* Latin for **a wonder** or **marvel**

8. _____ : *makhazin;* Arabic for **storehouses**

acrobat!

TRY THIS! Use a dictionary to find the origins of the following words: *encyclopedia, automobile, furniture.*

Harcourt

▶ **Find the independent and dependent clauses in these sentences. Draw one line under each independent clause. Draw two lines under each dependent clause.**

1. After the goose laid eight eggs, seven eggs hatched.

2. When Avery fought Fern, he broke an egg.

3. After the eggs hatched, the gander was proud.

4. The goose was very busy because she had goslings to take care of.

▶ **Rewrite each sentence. Add the kind of clause shown in parentheses ( ). Remember to add commas as needed.**

5. Templeton took the egg _____. **(dependent)**

_____

6. After the goose honked _____. **(independent)**

_____

7. _____ because Fern tossed them some corn. **(independent)**

_____

8. _____ the goose returned to her nest. **(dependent)**

_____

TRY THIS! Write a paragraph telling what happens after the ending of "Charlotte's Web." Include dependent clauses in at least three sentences. Draw one line under the independent clauses and two lines under the dependent clauses in the sentences you write.

Name_____

▶ **Write a Spelling Word to complete each sentence.**

1. I _____ for hidden spiderwebs.

2. I wonder how that spider _____
   to make a web.

3. I admire each _____ in the web.

4. The spider seems to work hard, as if making a web

   were an _____ task.

5. Spiders have taken the art of weaving

   _____ than we can imagine.

6. That spider has _____ my admiration.

> **SPELLING WORDS**
>
> 1. curve
> 2. learned
> 3. curly
> 4. pearl
> 5. purse
> 6. further
> 7. turtle
> 8. urgent
> 9. burning
> 10. search
> 11. earth
> 12. earned

▶ **Write a Spelling Word to complete the phrase about each picture.**

7. Aunt Jo's

   _____

8. a _____
   candle

9. _____
   hair

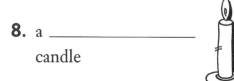

10. a _____
    necklace

11. our home, the

    _____

12. a _____

Handwriting Tip: Bring the last downstroke of *u* to the bottom writing line, or it might look like *v*. Write the Spelling Words below.

13. curly _____

14. purse _____

15. turtle _____

16. urgent _____

Harcourt

Name _____

▶ Write the word from the tree top that matches each
definition. The message in the shaded area beside the tree
trunk tells you who hangs out in trees. Two words are used twice.

endangered   smuggled   jealous   manageable

displeasure   facial   coordination

1. angry that another
has what you do not

_ _ _ _ _ _ _

2. disapproval

_ _ _ _ _ _ _ _ _ _

3. of the face

_ _ _ _ _

4. close to not
existing anymore

_ _ _ _ _ _ _ _ _ _

5. able to be handled

_ _ _ _ _ _ _ _

6. taken secretly

_ _ _ _ _ _ _

7. the smooth
movement of parts

_ _ _ _ _ _ _ _ _ _ _ _

8. unhappiness

_ _ _ _ _ _ _ _ _ _

9. able to be
controlled

_ _ _ _ _ _ _ _ _ _

Harcourt

SCHOOL-HOME CONNECTION With your child, talk about ways
people and animals interact. Use at least three Vocabulary Words.

Touch a Dream   **67**

Name _____

▶ Fill in the first two columns of the K-W-L chart. Then use
information from the story to fill in the last column.

K	W	L
What I Know	**What I Want to Know**	**What I Learned**

▶ Make a list of five rules for babysitting a baby orangutan. Think about the
most important needs that an orangutan has.

1. _____

2. _____

3. _____

4. _____

5. _____

Harcourt

▶ **Fill in the notepad with notes about each passage.**

1. Prairie dogs are social animals. This means that they live together in family groups. Prairie dogs live in underground "towns." Different family groups have their own "neighborhoods," with many different underground rooms connected by tunnels. Some rooms are for sleeping, and others are for storing food. Some are nurseries, where young prairie dogs are raised.

2. Prairie dog "towns" include listening posts above ground. There, the animals listen for enemies. When a prairie dog hears an enemy, it barks to warn others to hide. This barking noise gave the prairie dog its name, but the animal isn't really a dog. It is a type of ground squirrel.

3. Barking is just one of the sounds that prairie dogs make. Some-times they stand on their hind legs, throw their heads back, and give a whistling call. They may be signaling that no enemies are in sight, or they may be letting other prairie dogs know that this is their territory. Prairie dogs may jump straight up while they are whistling, and sometimes they even fall over backward!

Notepad

1. _____
   _____
   _____
   _____
   _____
   _____

2. _____
   _____
   _____
   _____
   _____
   _____

3. _____
   _____
   _____
   _____
   _____

Harcourt

Name _____

▶ **Fill in the notepad with notes about each passage.**

1. Underground prairie dog towns make good homes because they are cooler in summer and warmer in winter than the air above. Since the underground rooms are comfortable and safe, other animals make use of them.

2. Burrowing owls sometimes move into prairie dog holes. They make nests there, lay eggs, and hatch their young in a home they didn't even have to build! Burrowing owls may take over holes dug by other animals, too, such as badgers or skunks.

3. During hot weather, rattlesnakes often move into prairie dog burrows to keep cool. When this happens, the prairie dogs don't always move out. Instead, they may just build a wall between the snake's room and the rest of the burrow. Prairie dog burrows are popular with rattlesnakes during the winter, too. Dozens of them may hibernate in a cozy room.

Notepad

1. _____

_____

_____

_____

_____

2. _____

_____

_____

_____

3. _____

_____

_____

_____

_____

_____

Harcourt

TRY THIS! Read a magazine or encyclopedia article about an animal that interests you. Take notes on the article so you can share the information with someone at home.

70 Touch a Dream

Name _____

▶ **Read the following paragraphs. Then complete the outline below.**

Many wild animals provide places for their babies to stay safe while they are young and helpless. One kind of shelter is a hole or cave called a *den*. Foxes dig dens. Their pups are born there and live there while they are growing up. Wolves also dig dens, sometimes with the help of other adult wolves in the pack. Coyotes use dens, too, but sometimes they take over another animal's burrow and make it larger.

Some kinds of birds protect their young in tunnels. Atlantic puffins dig into grassy land near the sea. Bee-eaters peck holes in a cliff and make them larger until they have long tunnels. Kingfishers dig their tunnels in the banks of streams.

Other birds make tree holes for their babies. Screech owls don't peck out their own holes. Instead, they find a natural hollow spot in a tree or a hole made by another bird. Woodpeckers make their own tree holes.

Shelters for Baby Animals

I. Dens

    A. _____

    B. _____

    C. _____

II. Tunnels

    A. _____

    B. _____

    C. _____

III. Tree holes

    A. _____

       1. Don't make their own holes

       2. _____

    B. _____

Harcourt

Name _____

▶ **Read the following paragraphs. Then complete the outline.**

Bird parents work hard to bring up their babies. Since many newly hatched birds have no feathers, the adult birds must keep the bodies of their young the right temperature. Parents huddle over the young birds to keep them warm when the weather is cool. In hot weather, they may spread their wings over the babies to give them shade.

Of course, parents must feed their babies. Baby birds eat quite often. Their parents make many trips back and forth to the nest, bringing food.

Another important job of the parents is to protect their young from danger. They may try to chase away a predator. At other times, they may try to distract the predator. To do this, they let the predator see the parent go in the opposite direction from the nest. Often, the parent will make itself look injured. All this display is to try to get the predator to follow the parent away from the baby birds.

Parents Bringing Up Baby Birds

I. Must keep them the right temperature

   A. _____

   B. _____

II. _____

   A. Babies eat quite often.

   B. _____

III. _____

   A. _____

   B. Distract an enemy so it follows parent away from babies

      1. _____

      2. _____

TRY THIS! Find and read an interesting nonfiction passage in a book or magazine in your classroom. Outline the article to help you remember the information. Start with the topic headings and add the details.

Harcourt

Name _____

▶ Label each sentence *simple, compound,* or *complex.*

1. Orangutans are sweet, but they have sharp

   teeth. _____

2. When I met Nanang, he

   was very young. _____

3. Nanang will return to the forest. _____

4. After he returns to the forest, my job is done.

   _____

▶ **Draw one line under each independent clause. Draw two lines under each dependent clause.**

5. Since Nanang does not have his mother, he needs the babysitter.

6. Although he is young, he is quite strong.

▶ **Combine each pair of sentences into a complex sentence. The connecting words in the box may help you.**

after	because	since	when
although	before	if	while

7. Nanang held my hand. We walked in the forest.

   _____

   _____

8. Nanang is so young. He is in danger from snakes.

   _____

   _____

   _____

SCHOOL-HOME CONNECTION Have your child write a short paragraph about his or her different chores at home. The paragraph should include at least two complex sentences.

Name _____

▶ **The letters of the underlined words are mixed up. Write the correct Spelling Words on the lines.**

1. The orangutans
   formed a <u>occunli</u>.   _____

2. They sit on the <u>drgonu</u>.   _____

3. They talk <u>taoub</u>
   problems.   _____

4. Does that <u>kcbagorudn</u>
   noise bother them?   _____

5. They hold their
   next meeting in
   the city, <u>wwnndtoo</u>.   _____

6. Then they can
   spread their papers
   out on a <u>treocnu</u>.   _____

SPELLING WORDS
1. ground
2. frown
3. downtown
4. bounced
5. council
6. about
7. scout
8. counter
9. background
10. amount
11. bound
12. shower

▶ **Write the Spelling Word that rhymes with each word below.**

7. sound   _____

8. shout   _____

9. pounced   _____

10. town   _____

11. flower   _____

12. count   _____

Handwriting Tip: Make sure each letter is
the correct size. Similar kinds of letters should be
the same size. Write the Spelling Words below.

13. council _____   15. amount _____

14. bound   _____   16. downtown _____

74 Touch a Dream

Name _____

▶ **Read the words in the box. Write the word that best completes each analogy.**

| alarmed | windbreak | conch | paddock | rustle |

1. *Apple* is to *fruit* as _____ is to *seashell.*

2. *Happy* is to *pleased* as *frightened* is to _____.

3. *Loud* is to *shout* as *soft* is to _____.

4. *Windshield* is to *glass* as _____ is to *trees.*

5. *Pen* is to *pigs* as _____ is to *horses.*

▶ **Choose the word from the box above that matches each clue. Write the word in the puzzle.**

Down

6. a soft, whispering noise

7. a line of trees

8. a fenced field for horses

Across

9. frightened

10. a type of seashell

TRY THIS! Make a list of things you might see and do if you visited a farm or a beach. Use at least two Vocabulary Words.

Harcourt

Name _____

Skill Reminder   *I, me, we, us, our, ours, my, mine* = first person

he, she, him, his, her, hers, they, them, their, theirs = third person

▶ Read each sentence and write *first person* or *third person* to tell the point of view. Then write one pronoun from the sentence that helped you identify the point of view.

When my family and I were pioneers in Nebraska, I went to a school built of bales of straw.

1. Point of view: _____

2. Pronoun clue: _____

Our building didn't last long, because it caught fire late one night.

3. Point of view: _____

4. Pronoun clue: _____

Many pioneer families wanted their children to learn to read and write.

5. Point of view: _____

6. Pronoun clue: _____

Students usually didn't have desks, and they sat on benches, not chairs.

7. Point of view: _____

8. Pronoun clue: _____

We were often cold and uncomfortable, but we were glad for the chance to learn.

9. Point of view: _____

10. Pronoun clue: _____

TRY THIS! Look back at a story you have read this year. On a separate sheet of paper, write the story title. Then tell the point of view the writer used. List some clues that help you identify the point of view.

Harcourt

Name _____

▶ Complete the character map below. Write important information about each of the characters.

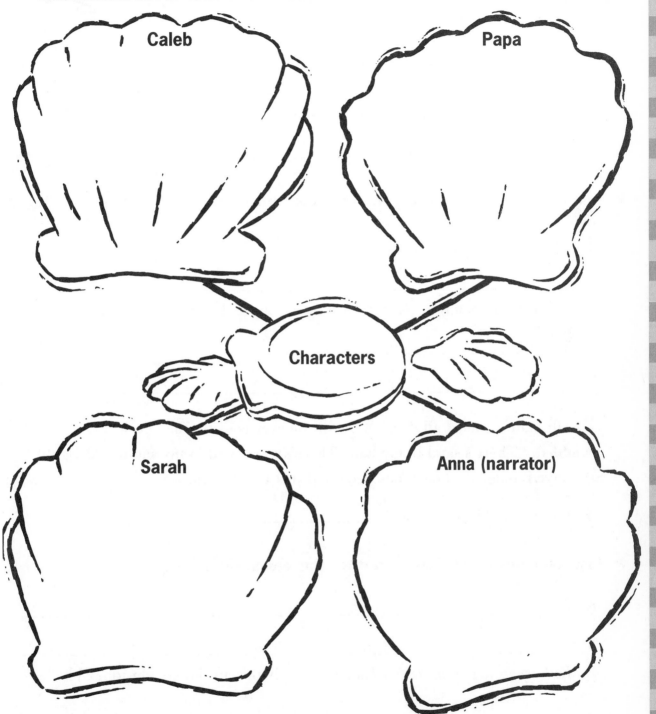

Caleb

Papa

Characters

Sarah

Anna (narrator)

▶ Write a one-sentence summary telling what effect Sarah has on the family.

_____

_____

Harcourt

Name _____

▶ **Read each paragraph. Use information in the paragraph and your own knowledge to draw conclusions about the character. Then write the answer to each question.**

Mindy wiggled her toes in the sand happily and looked out at the ocean. The cool breeze and warm sand made her smile. How much fun it was to splash in the water! She wished the day would never end.

1. Does Mindy like the beach? _____

▶ **List the clues that helped you draw this conclusion.**

2. _____

3. _____

4. *Mindy wants to stay at the beach as long as possible.* Is this a valid conclusion?

Why? _____

_____

Kelli hadn't smiled all day. "Why did we ever come to the beach?" she grumbled. "There's sand in my hair. There's even sand in my sandwich! Ugh!" She stayed under the beach umbrella and just took a nap.

5. Does Kelli like the beach? _____

▶ **List the clues that helped you draw this conclusion.**

6. _____

7. _____

8. *Kelli wants to stay on the beach a long time.* Is this a valid conclusion? Why?

_____

_____

TRY THIS! Think about another story you have read this year that you enjoyed. What conclusion can you make about how one of the characters felt?

Harcourt

Name _____

▶ **Read the paragraph. Then choose the best answer for each question, and mark the letter for that answer.**

How can you build a house if you don't have any wood or bricks? In the early 1900s farmers in Nebraska used hay because it was easy to find. Machines pressed the dried hay and tied it into blocks called *bales*. These bales of hay were each about four feet long and two feet wide. With the help of their neighbors, farmers would stack the bales of hay to make walls. They knew that they could add wooden floors and shingle roofs later, when they might be able to get wood. Hay houses were fairly warm in winter, but people living in them had to be careful of fire, since hay burns easily. Hay walls were also good places for fleas to live.

1 Farmers in Nebraska grew _____.

A many fruit trees

B large oak trees

C a lot of hay

D no crops at all

2 What information helped you decide how to answer question 1?

F Farmers had so much hay that they could use it for building houses.

G There was plenty of fruit.

H There was plenty of wood.

J It took a long time to build a house.

3 Farmland in Nebraska had _____.

A many trees

B very few trees

C many brick factories

D not enough hay

4 What information helped you decide how to answer question 3?

F Bales of hay were very heavy.

G There weren't many bricks.

H Farmers ran out of hay.

J People didn't have enough wood to build houses.

5 Farmers in Nebraska in the early 1900s _____.

A always worked alone

B depended on neighbors for help

C had money to buy everything they wanted

D didn't get along with their neighbors

Answers
1 Ⓐ Ⓑ Ⓒ Ⓓ
2 Ⓕ Ⓖ Ⓗ Ⓙ
3 Ⓐ Ⓑ Ⓒ Ⓓ
4 Ⓕ Ⓖ Ⓗ Ⓙ
5 Ⓐ Ⓑ Ⓒ Ⓓ

Harcourt

Name _____

▶ **On each line, write the phrase that means the opposite of the underlined phrase in the sentence.**

1. When a new person came by, the kitten was <u>quiet and shy</u>.
   noisy and friendly   *OR*   **silent and meek**

   _____

2. Jack made a little clay bowl that was <u>round and perfect</u>.
   beautifully circular   *OR*   **lopsided and flawed**

   _____

3. When Jenny finished washing and combing her hair, it was <u>straight and wet</u>.
   snarled and dry   *OR*   **shiny and slick**

   _____

4. Rebecca wanted the <u>smoothest and whitest</u> piece of marble she could find.
   roughest and dirtiest   *OR*   **finest and clearest**

   _____

5. The creek water was <u>cool and sparkling</u> around Sarah's ankles.
   warm and dark   *OR*   **cold and bright**

   _____

6. When it came out of the dryer, the laundry was <u>warm and dry</u>.
   cool and damp   *OR*   **hot and fuzzy**

   _____

7. Jim's Grandma was always <u>calm and kind</u>.
   pleasant and nice   *OR*   **nervous and mean**

   _____

8. The last piece of sandpaper left was <u>large and rough</u>.
   big and gritty   *OR*   **tiny and smooth**

   _____

TRY THIS! Write a short paragraph describing a place you would like to visit. Then use a thesaurus to find antonyms for each descriptive word. Use these words to write a paragraph describing a place you would never want to visit.

Harcourt

Name _____

▶ Write *common* or *proper* to identify each underlined noun.

1. The <u>sheep</u> ran in the field. _____

2. As we waited, <u>Caleb</u> played with a marble. _____

3. Suddenly he saw a yellow <u>bonnet</u>. _____

4. Papa's wagon was pulled by <u>Jack</u> and Old Bess. _____

5. Sarah brought <u>Seal,</u> a gray cat with white feet. _____

▶ For each sentence, fill in the blank with a common noun.

6. We watched the wagon with _____ in our hearts.

7. The wagon passed the _____ and then stopped.

8. One of Sarah's gifts was a(n) _____.

9. Sarah told my _____, Caleb, about gulls.

10. Sarah's room had a(n) _____ in it.

▶ Complete each sentence by writing a proper noun in the blank.

11. Before he left, _____ combed his hair.

12. Sarah gave Caleb's sister, _____, a sea stone.

13. Did the stone really come from the state of _____?

14. Lottie and _____ stared at Sarah's cat.

15. _____ stepped out of her case and purred.

TRY THIS! Write a paragraph about a time when someone visited your family. Use both common and proper nouns.

Harcourt

Name _____

▶ **Write the Spelling Word that fits each clue.**

1. This person could
give you a job. _____

2. It would make you
very sick. _____

3. It describes something
ruined. _____

4. Make decisions
about these. _____

5. When your friends
speak, they use these. _____

6. It describes an egg
cooked in water. _____

SPELLING WORDS
1. *boiled*
2. *annoyed*
3. *choices*
4. *poison*
5. *employer*
6. *joining*
7. *spoiled*
8. *voices*
9. *destroyed*
10. *pointing*
11. *avoided*
12. *enjoying*

▶ **Write a Spelling Word to complete each sentence.**

Dad was **(7)** _____ that it was raining.

It **(8)** _____ his plans. He was

(9) _____ his day off, but now he

(10) _____ anything outdoors. I was

(11) _____ to a video, hoping he

would be **(12)** _____ me soon.

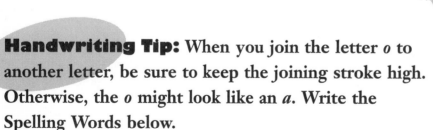

Handwriting Tip: When you join the letter *o* to
another letter, be sure to keep the joining stroke high.
Otherwise, the *o* might look like an *a*. Write the
Spelling Words below.

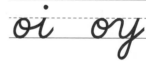

13. annoyed _____ **15.** spoiled _____

14. pointing _____ **16.** enjoying _____

Harcourt

Name _____

▶ **Use words from the boxes to complete the sentences in the story. Two words will be used twice.**

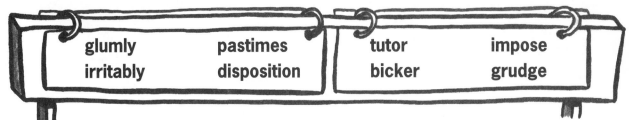

| glumly | pastimes | tutor | impose |
| irritably | disposition | bicker | grudge |

Bill's friend was late. Bill felt disappointed as he sat waiting

(1) _____ in front of the TV.

Just then his cousin, Dave, came in. He looked annoyed. "Two members of the Little League team have decided to take up soccer and tennis

as their **(2)** _____ instead of baseball," Dave said

(3) _____. He asked Bill to play on the baseball team.

Bill began to **(4)** _____ with Dave and told him to leave

him alone. His normally happy **(5)** _____ was clouded because he was upset that his friend was late. Dave saw that Bill was in a bad mood.

He didn't want to **(6)** _____, so he left.

But as he walked away, Dave felt he had better come to an understanding with Bill. He didn't want a senseless

(7) _____ to build up between them that would carry bad feelings. So he went back inside and asked Bill if there was a problem he could help with. Bill told him about his friend being late. Dave replied, "We can fix that. When he arrives,

we'll both **(8)** _____ him in how to tell time!"

Bill couldn't help but laugh. His cheerful **(9)** _____

showed again. He told Dave he would gladly consider baseball as one

of his **(10)** _____.

TRY THIS! Think of another story you have read that involves a family situation. Describe the story, using at least three Vocabulary Words.

Harcourt

Name _____

Skill Reminder	clues in text + what you already know = conclusion

▶ **Read the sentences and write the correct conclusions on the lines. Then write about the clue that helped you.**

Marisa Hernández and her mother show their pet goat in competitions. Marisa's pets also include two dogs, a rabbit, a lamb, and a pony.

1. Which conclusion can you draw?

   a. Marisa likes goats better than lambs.

   b. Marisa likes many different kinds of animals.

_____

2. Clue: _____

Kevin Lockhart reads a story to his three-year-old sister, Ashley. "I want Ashley to learn to love books as much as I do," Kevin says.

3. Which conclusion can you draw?

   a. Kevin doesn't like to spend time with his sister.

   b. Kevin has learned that reading can be fun.

_____

4. Clue: _____

Maylee Chen shows her prize-winning rock collection. It took Maylee three years to collect and identify all these rocks.

5. Which conclusion can you draw?

   a. Maylee runs out of patience in a hurry.

   b. Maylee sticks with a project once she starts it.

_____

6. Clue: _____

TRY THIS! Make a list of conclusions you can draw about a person you know or a character you have read about.

Harcourt

Name _____

▶ **Complete the cause-and-effect fishbone.**

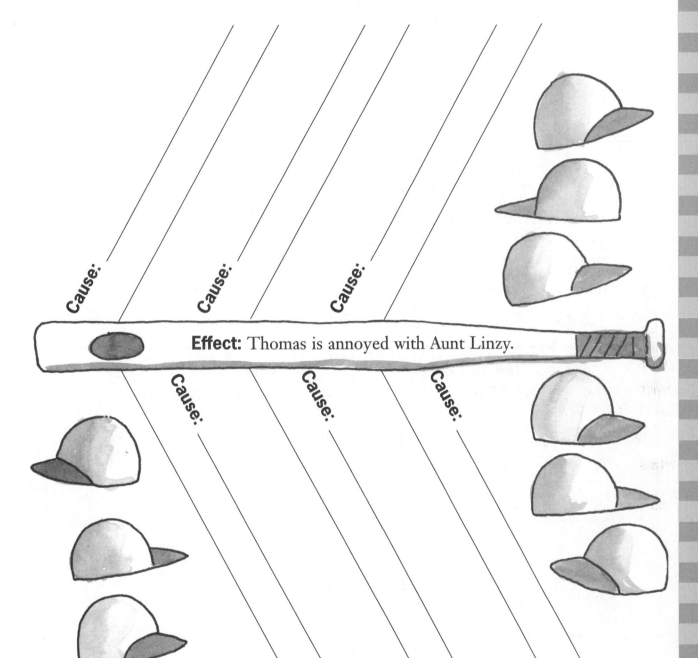

Cause:

Cause:

Cause:

Effect: Thomas is annoyed with Aunt Linzy.

Cause:

Cause:

Cause:

▶ **Write a one-sentence summary telling how Grandfather's feelings about Aunt Linzy compare with Thomas's feelings.**

_____

_____

_____

Harcourt

Name _____

▶ **Read the passage. Then complete the chart to show five ways Derek and Kyle are alike and five ways they are different.**

   Derek wasn't sure he wanted his cousin Kyle to spend the summer with him and his family. Both boys were baseball fans, but Derek cheered for the Pirates and Kyle was a fan of the Giants. Kyle didn't like cats, and Derek loved his pet kittens. "I talk a lot, and he's so quiet. He doesn't like to go to movies like I do. It's good that we both like to swim," Derek thought, "but I like to go out with Uncle Bill on his sailboat. Kyle doesn't know the first thing about sailing. We'll both enjoy eating the fish we catch, though."

   "Both of you like to play soccer," Uncle Bill reminded Kyle. "You're both good at board games, too. I'll bet you'll have some fun together after all."

Ways Derek and Kyle Are Alike	**Ways Derek and Kyle Are Different**
1. _____	6. _____
2. _____	7. _____
3. _____	8. _____
4. _____	9. _____
5. _____	10. _____

SCHOOL-HOME CONNECTION Talk with your child about two places you have been, such as a park, store, or someone's home. Ask your child to list ways the two places are alike and different.

Harcourt

Name _____

▶ **Write the simile from the box that best completes each sentence.**

like a baby	like a fool	like whipped cream
like the sun	like trees	like best friends
like a fish out of water	like a freight train	like day and night
like two peas in a pod		

1. The tornado was very loud. It sounded

_____.

2. I love to watch the clouds pile up on a summer day. They look

_____.

3. My little brother says broccoli looks

_____.

4. Rick forgot his lines in the school play. He felt

_____.

5. Rebecca's smiling face shines

_____.

6. Abbey and Erica are sisters and do everything together.

They are _____.

7. Julie felt very out of place at her new school.

She felt _____.

8. I went to bed the minute I got home from camping. I closed my

eyes and slept _____.

9. The twins looked exactly alike and always
wanted to do the same things. They were

_____.

10. He was outgoing and she was shy. They were

_____.

Harcourt

▶ **Draw one line under each noun. Write *S* above each singular noun and *P* above each plural noun.**

1. All the shells and a special fossil were in a box.

2. Many other boxes were on the porch.

3. My aunt will buy a dresser for her belongings.

4. Do the animals like the new visitor?

5. The boys got on their bicycles and went

   for a long ride.

▶ **Replace each blank with the plural form of the word in parentheses ( ). Then rewrite each sentence.**

6. The _____ finished the jigsaw puzzle. **(woman)** _____

   _____

7. "Baseball players earn big _____," Aunt Linzy said. **(salary)** _____

   _____

8. The guest did not want to catch _____. **(catfish)** _____

   _____

9. Did Aunt Linzy use _____ to cut vegetables? **(knife)** _____

   _____

10. When the _____ ran by, the cat showed its _____. **(mouse, tooth)** _____

   _____

SCHOOL-HOME CONNECTION Work with your child to make a list of fifteen nouns that name items found in the home. Write the singular and plural forms of each noun.

Harcourt

Name _____

▶ **Read this journal entry. Find and circle the twelve misspelled words. Then write the words correctly on the lines below.**

SPELLING WORDS

1. shelves
2. sheep
3. teeth
4. elves
5. mice
6. calves
7. spacecraft
8. jeans
9. feet
10. women
11. men
12. geese

Meen, wimen, and children were at the fair. Everyone wore geans. In the cooking tent, we passed shelfes with cakes. Then we went to see the animals and saw sheip and calvs. We looked at lots of chickens and giese, too. My fete ached.

The best part of the day began when an announcement came over the loudspeaker: "Ladies and gentlemen, the pie-eating contest is about to begin." I rushed over to enter. They had a hundred berry pies, each cut in half. I did my best, and my tieth turned pink, but I didn't win the prize. I did, however, eat enough to have a weird nightmare last night. I dreamed about teams of elfs and mise racing to the moon on two spacecrapht. No more pie for me!

1. _____ 7. _____

2. _____ 8. _____

3. _____ 9. _____

4. _____ 10. _____

5. _____ 11. _____

6. _____ 12. _____

Handwriting Tip: Bring the first upstroke of the letter *s* to a point, or it might look like an *a*. Write the Spelling Words below.

13. elves _____ **15.** calves _____

14. shelves _____ **16.** geese _____

Harcourt

Name _____

▶ **Read the words in the picnic basket. Then write the word**
that answers each riddle. Some words will be used twice.

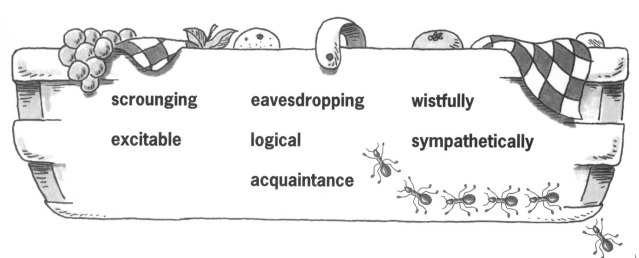

scrounging   eavesdropping   wistfully

excitable   logical   sympathetically

acquaintance

1. I look in a sad or longing way. I'm looking _____.

2. I overhear what you're saying. I'm _____.

3. It's easy to make me act wild. I'm _____.

4. I search through someone's junk. I'm _____.

5. I think in a way that makes sense. I'm _____.

6. I'm feeling sorry for you. I'm acting _____.

7. I'm getting to know you. I'm making your _____.

8. I borrow things from a pile of clothes. I'm _____.

9. I show a lot of emotion. I'm _____.

10. I'm listening at your keyhole. I'm _____.

TRY
THIS!
Imagine that you meet Tucker Mouse and Chester Cat. Write what you tell
them or ask them. Use at least three Vocabulary Words.

Harcourt

90 Touch a Dream

| Skill Reminder | compare = tell how two things are alike |
| | contrast = tell how they are different |

▶ **Read the paragraph. Then complete the Venn diagram to show ways in which the paintings were alike and different.**

At the art museum Brad saw two paintings of New York City. Both were scenes of Times Square, but *Winter in the City* showed falling snow. People walking along the sidewalks were bent against the wind. It was growing dark, and a newsstand near the corner was closed. Brad liked *Summertime* better. It also showed people on the sidewalks, but the noon sun was shining brightly. The same newspaper stand was open now. The two paintings were very different, but both made Brad feel the energy of the city.

Winter in the City

1. _____

_____

2. _____

_____

3. _____

_____

Both Paintings

4. _____

_____

5. _____

_____

6. _____

_____

Summertime

7. _____

_____

8. _____

_____

9. _____

_____

TRY THIS! Look at two of the illustrations in a story you have read. Choose two that are alike in some ways. Make a Venn diagram like the one on this page to compare and contrast the two.

Harcourt

Name _____

▶ As you read, start to fill in the prediction web. After you
read, write what actually happens.

Information from the Story	What I Already Know

Prediction

What Actually Happens

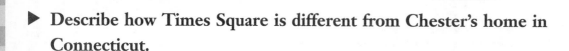

▶ Describe how Times Square is different from Chester's home in
Connecticut.

_____

_____

_____

Harcourt

Name _____

▶ **Read Susan's journal entry. Look for time-order words or phrases that help you know the order of the events. Circle each time-order word or phrase. Then answer the questions.**

I can't believe how exciting New York is! First, our plane arrived. Right after that, we took a taxi to our hotel. Then, we unpacked our suitcases and went out to explore. To begin, we just walked along Broadway. We were overwhelmed by the number of people and the number of cars. After that, we had lunch. Next, we walked east to Fifth Avenue to do some window-shopping. Then, we walked all the way to Central Park. After we got there, we bought ice cream for a snack. Later, we went back to our hotel room to rest. In the evening, we had dinner in the hotel. Finally, we went to see a Broadway musical. What a thrilling end to a wonderful day!

1. Where did Susan go just after arriving at the airport? _____

_____

2. What did she do just before going out to explore? _____

_____

3. Where did Susan walk at first? _____

_____

4. Where did Susan go after window-shopping? _____

_____

5. What did Susan do just before going to the theater? _____

_____

TRY THIS!

Write about a place you might like to visit, and list a day's events.

Harcourt

Name _____

▶ **Read the paragraphs. Then choose the best answer for each question. Mark the letter for that answer.**

Ahmed's trip from Texas to New York was a long one. First, he drove to the airport in Houston. Then, he boarded a plane. The plane landed at Love Field, near downtown Dallas. Next, he took a bus to the Dallas Airport. From there he took a flight to New York.

When the plane was in the air, Ahmed had lunch. Two hours later the plane landed. Finally, Ahmed reached New York.

1 First, Ahmed _____.

A flew to Houston

B drove to Dallas

C drove to the Houston airport

D took a taxi to the airport

2 Next, Ahmed _____.

F boarded a plane

G took a bus ride

H flew to Dallas Airport

J landed in New York

3 After the plane took off from Houston, _____.

A Ahmed ate breakfast

B the plane flew into a storm

C the plane returned to Houston

D the plane landed at Love Field

4 At Dallas Airport, Ahmed _____.

F took a taxi

G boarded a plane for New York

H took a bus ride

J drove back home

5 What happened next?

A Ahmed had lunch.

B Ahmed saw a movie.

C Ahmed felt the plane begin to land.

D Ahmed landed in New York.

6 What happened last?

F Ahmed landed in Houston.

G Ahmed arrived in New York.

H Ahmed left Houston.

J Ahmed landed at Dallas Airport.

Answers

1 Ⓐ Ⓑ Ⓒ Ⓓ	4 Ⓕ Ⓖ Ⓗ Ⓙ
2 Ⓕ Ⓖ Ⓗ Ⓙ	5 Ⓐ Ⓑ Ⓒ Ⓓ
3 Ⓐ Ⓑ Ⓒ Ⓓ	6 Ⓕ Ⓖ Ⓗ Ⓙ

Harcourt

Name _____

▶ **Rewrite each phrase, using a possessive noun.**

1. the adventure of the hero

_____

2. the song of the children

_____

3. the meadow belonging to the rabbits

_____

4. the story of the class

_____

5. the nest of the mice

_____

▶ **Rewrite each sentence, using the possessive form of the noun in parentheses ( ). Then write the plural possessive form of that noun.**

6. The _____ voice was strong and steady. **(cricket)**

_____

_____

7. Chester was carried to the city in the _____ picnic basket. **(family)**

_____

_____

8. The _____ newsstand became his new home. **(man)**

_____

_____

TRY THIS! Write a paragraph that describes your neighborhood. Use three singular possessive nouns and two plural possessive nouns. Exchange paragraphs with a classmate to check each other's use of possessive nouns.

Name _____

▶ **Complete the second phrase so that it has the same meaning as the first.**

SPELLING WORDS

1. the nest
   of a bird   a _____ nest
2. a rider of
   a horse   a _____ rider
3. the tracks
   of a wolf   a _____ tracks
4. the hats of
   the girls   the _____ hats
5. the roots of
   two trees   two _____ roots
6. a friend of
   his parents   his _____ friend
7. the idea of
   the students   the _____ idea
8. the athletes
   of the class   the _____ athletes

1. *team's*
2. *players'*
3. *bird's*
4. *wolf's*
5. *horse's*
6. *class's*
7. *group's*
8. *girls'*
9. *students'*
10. *trees'*
11. *parents'*
12. *owners'*

▶ **Write the correct Spelling Word.**

9. of the team   _____
10. of the group   _____
11. of the owners   _____
12. of the players   _____

Handwriting Tip: Use equal spacing between letters. Leave one pencil-width between words. Write the Spelling Words below.

the wolf's den

13. players' _____   15. students' _____

14. horse's _____   16. class's _____

Name _____

▶ **Write a word from the box to complete each sentence.**

| tundra | ceases | bonding | piteously | surrender | abundant |

1. The _____ is so cold and empty!

4. No matter what happens, do not _____ to the cold. You must return with food.

2. Be brave. Stop howling so _____!

5. Our pups are _____ as they play together.

3. I'll go hunting so we'll have _____ food.

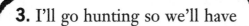

6. For those pups, the fun never _____!

▶ **Write the word from the box above that means the _opposite_ of each word.**

7. scarce _____

9. victory _____

8. begins _____

10. proudly _____

TRY THIS! Choose an animal you would like to be. Describe your day as that animal, using at least two Vocabulary Words.

Harcourt

Name _____

Skill Reminder **Look for time-order words to give you clues about the order in which events happen.**

▶ **Read the paragraph. Then complete each sentence to tell the order of the events.**

Crocodiles may look fierce, but they take good care of their young. The female crocodile begins her mothering by burying her eggs in a soft, sandy riverbank. Next, she guards them for three months so other animals won't bother them. When it's time for the eggs to hatch, the babies call to the mother. She hears their calls and uncovers the eggs. Then, she breaks the shells with her mouth. After all the eggs have hatched, the mother carries the babies in her mouth to shallow water. Then, she lets the babies go. They will live in this safe place for several weeks with their mother nearby. Finally, they will be able to take care of themselves. They will live up to seventy years.

The first thing a mother crocodile does to care for her eggs is

to **(1)** _____. Next, she

(2) _____. She uncovers

the eggs when **(3)** _____, and she

(4) _____. As soon as all the eggs

have hatched, she **(5)** _____. After

they reach the water, she **(6)** _____.

For several weeks the babies will **(7)** _____.

Finally, the baby crocodiles **(8)** _____.

Harcourt

SCHOOL-HOME CONNECTION With your child, talk about a special celebration in your family or community. Help your child use time-order words to list the order in which the events took place.

Name _____

▶ Fill in the first two columns of the K-W-L chart. Then use information from the story to fill in the last column.

K	W	L
What I Know	What I Want to Know	What I Learned

▶ Write a brief description of how wolf pups change during their first year.

_____

_____

_____

Harcourt

▶ **Read the paragraphs and the questions on this page and the next page. Then use the QAR (Question-Answer Relationship) strategy. Write a strategy from the box to answer each question.**

Right There	**Think and Search**	**On My Own**
(in text)	(inferred from text)	(prior knowledge or research)

Can you guess what animal can travel the length of a minivan in just one hop? It's the kangaroo. Kangaroos, which are marsupials, use their strong tails for balance when they hop. When they land, their tails help prop them up. Kangaroos usually move about by taking smaller leaps. The average jump is about six feet. Kangaroos can crawl, too. When they are grazing, they crawl awkwardly on all four feet.

In what two ways can kangaroos move about?

1. Strategy: _____

2. Answer: _____

_____

Why would it be hard for a kangaroo to jump if it didn't have a tail?

3. Strategy: _____

4. Answer: _____

_____

What is a marsupial?

5. Strategy: _____

6. Answer: _____

_____

GO ON

Name _____

A baby kangaroo is called a joey. When a joey is born, it still can't survive outside the mother's pouch. It isn't much bigger than your thumbnail. It has no hair and can't see, but its front legs are already strong. Soon after birth it begins crawling toward the mother's pouch. The joey makes the six-inch trip to the pouch in about three minutes. When it reaches the pouch, it begins feeding on milk. The pouch will be the joey's home for the next six months.

Why does a newborn joey need to have strong front legs?

1. Strategy: _____

2. Answer: _____

_____

Kangaroos come in many different sizes. The red kangaroo may grow to six feet tall, but the musky rat kangaroo is only about the size of a rabbit. In between are the wallaroos and the smaller wallabies. There are more than 45 different types of kangaroos.

Which kind of kangaroo is the smallest?

3. Strategy: _____

4. Answer: _____

_____

What are wallaroos like?

5. Strategy: _____

6. Answer: _____

_____

_____

![TRY THIS!] Think of an animal you know something about. Write as many questions as you can about that animal. Make a list of places a person might look to find the answers.

Harcourt

▶ Use one or more test-taking strategies in the box to answer each question from the choices below. Then write the letters of the strategies you used to answer the question.

A. Find and use key words.	**C. Check back to the paragraph.**
B. Eliminate wrong or silly answers.	**D. Use signal word *who* or *where*.**

Imagine living part of your life in the water and part on land! That's what seals, sea lions, and walruses do. They are *pinnipeds*, which means "fin-footed." Pinnipeds are skillful and graceful swimmers, but they look awkward as they waddle along on land, using their flippers as feet. In the sea, they must come to the surface to breathe, since they are mammals, who breathe air.

Where do seals, sea lions, and walruses live?

1. Answer: _____

on land   **both on land and in water**   **in the air**

2. Strategies used: _____

What does the word *pinniped* mean?

3. Answer: _____

seal   **without fins**   **fin-footed**

4. Strategies used: _____

Why do pinnipeds walk awkwardly?

5. Answer: _____

They can't swim.   **They use flippers.**   **They are fish.**

6. Strategies used: _____

Why can't pinnipeds breathe under water?

7. Answer: _____

They are mammals.   **They don't have noses.**   **They waddle.**

8. Strategies used: _____

Harcourt

Name _____

▶ **Rewrite each item, using abbreviations.**

1. 22 ounces _____

2. Mister Stephen Washburn _____

3. 35 miles, 25 feet _____

4. 62 Central Avenue _____

5. 6.4 kilometers _____

6. Friday, February 25 _____

▶ **Circle the correct abbreviation for each item.**

7. Snowy Boulevard	Snowy Blvd.	*OR*	Snowy Bd.
8. 30 centimeters	30 cm	*OR*	30 cms.
9. Tuesday, April 12	T'day., Ap. 12	*OR*	Tues., Apr. 12
10. 5 hours	5 hrs	*OR*	5 hr

Harcourt

TRY THIS! Write a story about a trip you would like to take. Use words that can be abbreviated. Share your story in a small group. See if your classmates can abbreviate your words correctly.

Name _____

▶ **Write the abbreviation for the underlined word.**

1. I was born in <u>September</u>.　_____

2. Dad saw the pups on <u>Friday</u>.　_____

3. On <u>Saturday</u> we saw a movie.　_____

4. We got a puppy in <u>December</u>.　_____

5. That pup weighs over a <u>pound</u>.　_____

6. Pups are fed from a <u>teaspoon</u>.　_____

SPELLING WORDS
1. Pres.
2. Dr.
3. Ave.
4. Hwy.
5. Rd.
6. St.
7. Fri.
8. Sat.
9. Sept.
10. Dec.
11. tsp.
12. lb.

▶ **Write the abbreviation of the word in parentheses.**

7. Coast _____ **(Highway)**

8. _____ Kwan **(Doctor)**

9. First _____ **(Street)**

10. _____ Taft **(President)**

11. 160 Bird _____ **(Avenue)**

12. 835 Rossi _____ **(Road)**

Handwriting Tip: When you write a capital letter, be sure it reaches the top writing line. Write the Spelling Words below.

$\mathcal{P}$

13. St. _____　**15.** Dec. _____

14. Ave. _____　**16.** Pres. _____

SCHOOL-HOME CONNECTION With your child, send letters to family members or friends whose addresses are different. Help your child write the envelopes using the correct abbreviations.

Harcourt

Name _____

▶ **Read the words below. Then read the words in groups on each cactus. Write the word that belongs in each group.**

| brush | spiny | teeming | habitat | topple | decomposes |

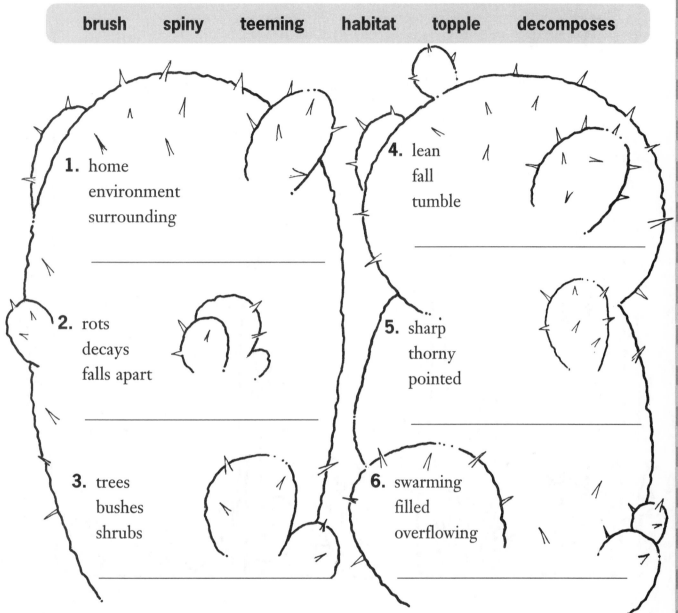

1. home
   environment
   surrounding

   _____

2. rots
   decays
   falls apart

   _____

3. trees
   bushes
   shrubs

   _____

4. lean
   fall
   tumble

   _____

5. sharp
   thorny
   pointed

   _____

6. swarming
   filled
   overflowing

   _____

▶ **Write a Vocabulary Word to complete each analogy.**

7. *Tree* is to *forest* as *bush* is to _____.

8. *Rain* is to *rainy* as *spine* is to _____.

9. *Goes* is to *stops* as *grows* is to _____.

10. *Film* is to *movie* as *home* is to _____.

SCHOOL-HOME CONNECTION With your child, talk about plants, flowers, and trees that grow nearby. Describe how they look, using at least two Vocabulary Words.

Touch a Dream **105**

Harcourt

Name _____

▶ Fill in the first two columns of the K-W-L chart. Then use
information from the story to fill in the last column.

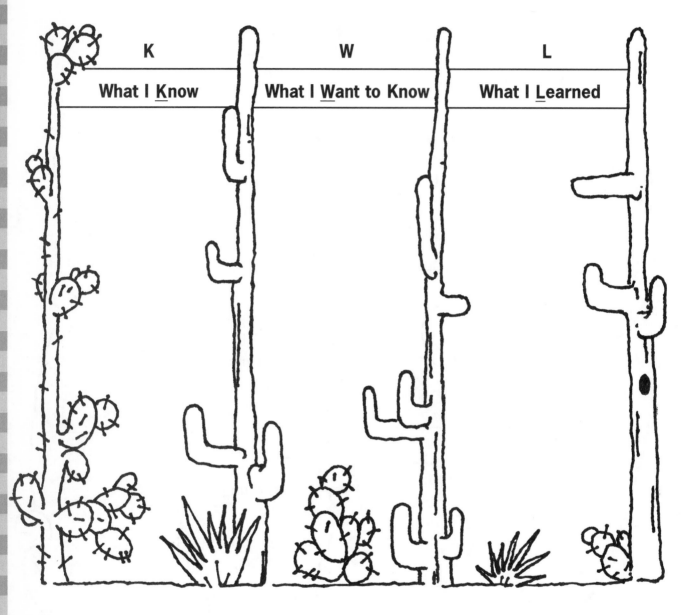

K	W	L
What I <u>K</u>now	What I <u>W</u>ant to Know	What I <u>L</u>earned

▶ List five ways in which the saguaro cactus helps desert animals.

1. _____

2. _____

3. _____

4. _____

5. _____

Harcourt

Name _____

▶ **Read the paragraph. Then answer the questions.**

Deserts do not have to be hot. They only have to be dry. Any area of land that gets ten inches or less of precipitation in a year is classified as a desert. Some deserts are very cold. Two of these cold deserts are at the North Pole and South Pole. Parts of the polar regions have a lot of water, but it is frozen all year long. Frozen water is not much help to plants and animals. Some of the Antarctic region is so cold and so high up that there is very little precipitation. *Precipitation* is any form of water that falls to earth. Rain, snow, sleet, and hail are kinds of precipitation.

1. This paragraph is an example of _____.
  a. fiction
  b. expository nonfiction
  c. persuasive nonfiction

2. What is the main purpose of the paragraph? _____

_____

3. Is the paragraph organized by main idea and details or by sequence of events?

_____

4. What is the main idea? _____

5. Which of these details supports the main idea? _____

_____

  a. Some deserts are very hot.
  b. Parts of the polar regions have a lot of water, but it is frozen all year long.
  c. Some polar regions have precipitation.

Name _____

▶ **Choose from the words or phrases below each line to complete each sentence. Write the answer on the line.**

The South American desert toad has adapted to life in the desert in an unusual way. When there is a rain shower in the summer, the toad absorbs moisture through its skin. Then it burrows into the mud. There it becomes inactive. Its heart rate slows down, and the animal is very still for months at a time. When rains come again, the

toad comes out of its underground home to find food. The female toad lays her eggs in a pool of rainwater. The baby toads hatch and develop. When the pool dries up, the babies burrow into the mud to wait for the rains to come again, just as their parents had done.

South American desert toad

Readers can tell that this paragraph is expository nonfiction because it gives

(1) _____ about the desert toad but does not

     stories   information   directions

(2) _____ .

     tell a story   give facts   give instructions

The main purpose of this paragraph is to

(3) _____ .

     give the author's opinion   persuade readers   give information

One clue that this paragraph is expository nonfiction is that it has a

(4) _____ along with it.

     heading   diagram   picture and caption

The paragraph is organized by

(5) _____ .

     main idea and details   sequence of events   giving directions

TRY THIS! Find a feature in a science textbook. List the clues that tell you if the feature is an example of expository nonfiction. Write whether it is organized according to main idea and details or sequence of events.

Harcourt

Name _____

▶ **Use the definitions in the Desert Dictionary to help you write labels for the saguaro cactus drawing.**

Desert Dictionary

boot   a hard wall that forms around holes in a
    cactus skin

flower   the part of a plant that has colorful
    petals and makes the plant's seeds

javelina   a desert hog that eats cactus roots

pleat   long fold on the skin of a cactus

pollen   a yellowish powder that fertilizes a plant

pulp   the soft, juicy part of a plant or fruit

seedling   young plant grown from seeds

spine   sharp, pointed growth on a plant

Fruit

1. _____

2. _____

3. _____

4. _____

5. _____

6. _____

7. _____

8. _____

Harcourt

Name _____

▶ **Underline the pronouns in these sentences. If a pronoun has an antecedent in the same sentence, draw an arrow from the pronoun to the antecedent.**

1. Darryl jumped when he saw a wolf spider.

2. Rita said, "I don't like spiders much, either."

3. Darryl saw a praying mantis and a lizard watching it.

4. Rita called to Darryl and showed him a hawk flying overhead.

5. Some birds hunt for lizards and eat them.

▶ **Rewrite these sentences, replacing the underlined words with pronouns.**

6. Rob walked up to the saguaro and took a close look at <u>the saguaro</u>. _____

_____

_____

7. "Marsha, come here," Rob called. "<u>Marsha</u> should see what <u>Rob</u> found."

_____

_____

8. "The inside of that hole is hard. Maybe <u>the hole</u> was a nest." _____

_____

9. "The hole might have given <u>a mother elf owl and her babies</u> a home." _____

_____

_____

10. Marsha replied, "Rob, maybe <u>Rob and Marsha</u> should call Ellie. <u>Ellie</u> would

like to see this." _____

_____

SCHOOL-HOME CONNECTION With your child, list the names of ten people that everyone in your family knows. Ask your child to write five pairs of sentences using a name in one sentence and a pronoun to replace it in the other sentence.

Harcourt

Name _____

▶ **The letters of the underlined words are mixed up. Write the correct Spelling Words on the lines.**

1. This cactus looks <u>drewi</u>. _____

2. I <u>libeeev</u> it's true. _____

3. I think the giant cactus is "<u>fceih</u>" among the desert plants. _____

4. Guess the <u>thewig</u> of this plant. _____

5. A <u>ecipe</u> of this cactus died. _____

6. We heard a <u>trgeifh</u> train. _____

7. Our <u>bgeniroh</u> has a cactus. _____

8. He'll <u>cireeve</u> a new plant. _____

SPELLING WORDS
1. weight
2. ceiling
3. field
4. reindeer
5. freight
6. eighteen
7. neighbor
8. receive
9. weird
10. chief
11. believe
12. piece

▶ **Write the Spelling Word that names each picture.**

9. _____

11. _____

10. _____

12. _____

Handwriting Tip: When you write the letter combination *ei* or *ie*, loop the *e* and not the *i*. Write the Spelling Words below. *ei*

13. weight _____

15. weird _____

14. field _____

16. piece _____

Harcourt

Name _____

▶ Write the word from the box that matches each clue below. The message in the shaded area of the answers tells you another name for an inventor.

document	prosthetic	device	disabilities
circular	scholarship	modify	

1. something made for a special use   _ _ _ _ _ _

2. round   _ _ _ _ _ _ _ _

3. an official paper or record   _ _ _ _ _ _ _ _

4. injuries or problems   _ _ _ _ _ _ _ _ _ _ _ _

5. artificial (body part)   _ _ _ _ _ _ _ _ _ _

6. to change   _ _ _ _ _ _

7. a student's knowledge   _ _ _ _ _ _ _ _ _ _ _

▶ Write the word from the box above that is related to each word below.

8. circle _____

9. unable _____

10. school _____

TRY THIS! Briefly describe an invention you think would help others. Use some Vocabulary Words.

▶ **Before you read, complete the first two columns of the SQ3R chart. Complete the third column during and after reading.**

Survey (page, heading)	Question	Read, Recite, Review (answer)
page 348		
page 350		
page 352		
page 354		

▶ **Write a one-sentence summary of the whole selection.**

_____

_____

Name _____

▶ **Read each paragraph. Then write the answers on the lines.**

Yo-yos are popular as toys and as items to collect, too. People in the United States have been playing with yo-yos since about 1929. Over the years children and adults have learned to do yo-yo tricks. Collectors often pay money for old wooden yo-yos or collect special models that whistle or glow in the dark.

1. What is the main idea? _____

_____

List three supporting details.

2. _____

3. _____

4. _____

The game of basketball developed over the years. In 1891 the "baskets" used as goals were actual peach baskets. When the ball landed in a basket, someone had to climb up and get the ball back out. Players eventually began to use a net with no bottom.

5. What is the main idea? _____

List two supporting details.

6. _____

7. _____

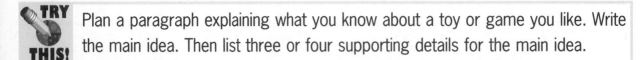

TRY THIS! Plan a paragraph explaining what you know about a toy or game you like. Write the main idea. Then list three or four supporting details for the main idea.

Harcourt

Name _____

▶ **Read the paragraphs. Then read each question, and decide
which is the best answer. Mark the letter for that answer.**

Dude ranching began more than a hundred years ago. Visitors from the East wanted to experience ranch life, so they went west and paid to stay on a ranch. The ranch hands called these visitors "dudes." In 1904 the Eaton family charged dudes $10 a week to stay and work on their ranch.

Today dude ranches are popular vacation spots for families, but guests don't do farm work! They can ride horseback or raft down a river. They may learn to twirl a rope or may take square-dancing lessons. Dude ranching is a way for ranchers to make extra money and for visitors to have fun.

1 Which sentence from the passage tells the main idea?

A Dude ranching began more than a hundred years ago.

B The ranch hands called these visitors "dudes."

C Dude ranching is a way for ranchers to make extra money and for visitors to have fun.

D They can ride horseback or raft down a river.

2 Which of these details supports the main idea?

F Dude ranching began more than a hundred years ago.

G Dude ranches are popular vacation spots for families.

H Guests don't know much about ranching.

J Guests must learn to ride horses.

3 Which of these details supports the main idea?

A Ranch hands called the visitors "dudes."

B Ranch hands taught dudes to round up cattle.

C Nobody had a dude ranch before 1882.

D Visitors would pay to stay on a ranch.

4 Which detail *does not* support the main idea?

F Ranchers charge visitors to come and stay.

G Dude ranching is still popular.

H Families have fun at dude ranches.

J Everybody likes river rafting.

Name _____

▶ **Read the directions for making a yarn animal. Then answer the questions.**

Materials:

▢ drawing paper	1/2 cup classroom glue
▱ pencil	1/4 cup water
▱ waxed paper	small foil pan or other container
4 paper clips	you can throw away
	thick yarn

Directions:

*Draw the outline of an animal so that every line
touches another line.*

Cover the drawing paper with waxed paper. Clip the two sheets together.

Mix glue and water in a disposable container.

*Cut a piece of yarn and soak it in the glue. Lift the yarn and squeeze so it
won't drip.*

Lay the strip of yarn along the drawn outline.

*Cut and soak other pieces of yarn, and add them to the design. Overlap the strips
so they will stick together.*

Let the yarn design dry overnight. Then remove it from the waxed paper.

1. Which should you do first, cut the yarn or soak it in glue?

_____

2. What should you do with the soaked yarn before you put it on the drawing?

_____

3. What may happen if you do not overlap the strips of yarn?

_____

4. How long should you let your yarn animal dry? _____

5. What is the last step? _____

6. What might happen if you do not follow the directions in order?

_____

SCHOOL-HOME CONNECTION Ask your child to write
directions for playing a game that two people can play.
Then follow the directions to play the game together.

Harcourt

Name _____

▶ **Rewrite each sentence, replacing the underlined word or
words with a pronoun. Write *subject* or *object* to identify
each pronoun you use.**

1. <u>Chester</u> made earmuffs for everyone. _____

_____

2. Mr. Parsons told Josh about <u>David Potter</u>. _____

_____

3. <u>Josh and David</u> worked together to design a glove. _____

_____

4. Soon David played for <u>the Spring Branch Mustangs</u>. _____

_____

5. <u>Reeba Daniel</u> invented a washer/dryer. _____

6. <u>Reba's invention</u> won a prize. _____

_____

▶ **Rewrite each sentence. Correct any errors in the use of pronouns.**

7. Josh and me helped David. _____

_____

8. David thanked me and Josh for helping. _____

_____

**TRY
THIS!** Write three separate sentences about an invention that you find useful.
Then put your sentences together in a paragraph, using pronouns to
replace nouns as needed.

Name _____

▶ **Write a Spelling Word to complete each sentence.**

1. Earn _____ with your own invention.

2. Invent a special knife to carve a_____.

3. The knives we _____ have are good.

4. Invent a new _____ stick.

5. Invent a machine to make a snack whenever you

   feel _____.

6. Invent a flying bike that goes from the

   _____ up to the mountaintop.

7. Invent a robot that moves like a _____.

SPELLING WORDS

1. tiny
2. hockey
3. heavy
4. every
5. money
6. turkey
7. early
8. hungry
9. already
10. valley
11. nobody
12. monkey

▶ **Write the Spelling Word that best means the
opposite of each word or phrase.**

8. light   _____

9. late   _____

10. everybody   _____

11. not one   _____

12. huge   _____

Handwriting Tip: Do not close the top of the
letter *y*, or it might look like *g*. Write the Spelling
Words below.

tiny

13. tiny _____   15. hockey _____

14. heavy _____   16. monkey _____

Harcourt

Name _____

▶ Write the word from the box that matches each clue.

| muttered | strengthening | sculptor |
| straightaway | retorted | alibi |

1. giving more energy to

2. one who makes statues

3. talked in a low voice

4. answered back

5. an excuse given
by one accused

6. immediately

▶ Write the word from the box above that means the *opposite* of each word.

7. asked _____

8. weakening _____

9. shouted _____

10. later _____

TRY THIS! Describe a time when you looked for something you lost. Tell what happened, using some Vocabulary Words.

Harcourt

Touch a Dream   **119**

Name _____

| Skill Reminder | main idea = central idea of the passage |
| | details = information about the main idea |

▶ **Read the paragraphs. Then answer the questions.**

When Abraham Lincoln was a boy, schools on the Kentucky frontier were very basic. Anyone who could read, write, and do simple arithmetic could be a teacher. There were few books, and paper was scarce. Often the students made their own arithmetic books. Children of different ages went to school in the same room.

1. What is the main idea? _____

_____

List three supporting details from the paragraph:

2. _____

3. _____

4. _____

Many children on the frontier had to walk long distances to school. School buildings often were not well heated. At home, the children studied by candlelight or by the light of the fireplace.

5. What is the main idea? _____

_____

6. Is the main idea stated in the paragraph? _____

List two supporting details from the paragraph:

7. _____

8. _____

Harcourt

SCHOOL-HOME CONNECTION With your child, discuss a book he or she enjoyed reading. Ask your child to tell the main idea of the book and give some important details.

Name _____

▶ Complete the character map below. Write important
information about each of the characters.

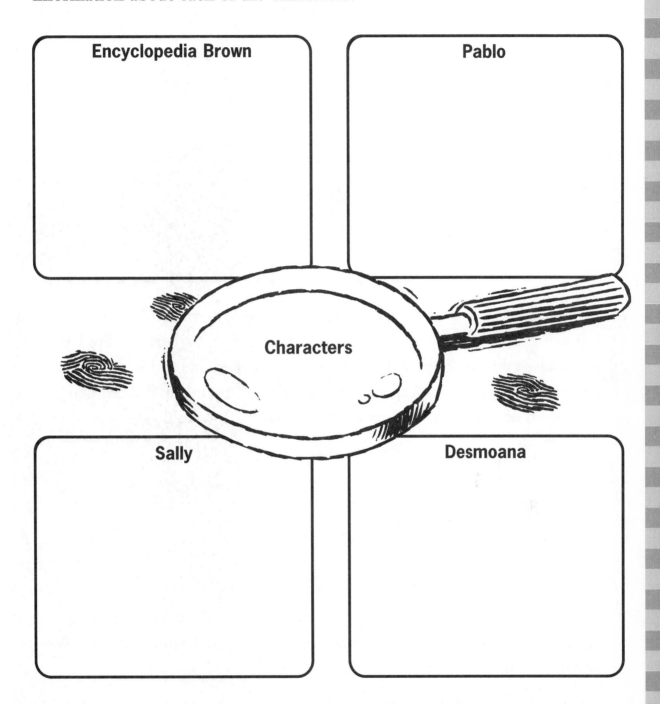

Encyclopedia Brown

Pablo

Characters

Sally

Desmoana

▶ Write a one-sentence summary explaining how Encyclopedia Brown
figures out that Desmoana is the thief.

_____

_____

Harcourt

Name _____

▶ **On the lines, write the answers to the questions.**

Beginning: Matt's mother, Mrs. Stevens, complains that paper clips are disappearing from her desk at home. Both Matt and his father say they haven't been borrowing any of them. Matt remembers that his pet bird, Pete, likes shiny things.

1. What is the problem in the story? _____

_____

2. What other information does Mrs. Stevens need to solve the problem?

_____

_____

Middle: Matt says he has been leaving Pete's cage door open when he leaves for school. Mrs. Stevens says she has noticed that the paper clips have disappeared during school hours. They look in Pete's cage and find a dime and a plastic ring, but no paper clips. Mr. Stevens says he has noticed that Pete often perches on a shelf above the fireplace.

3. What might the Stevens family do next to solve the problem? _____

_____

4. What makes you think that? _____

_____

Ending: Matt feels along the shelf but finds nothing. Then his hand bumps against a jar on the shelf. The jar falls, spilling paper clips onto the floor. Pete swoops down, chirping happily, and picks up a clip with his beak.

5. How is the problem solved? _____

_____

TRY THIS! Write a beginning for a mystery story. Be sure to state the problem. Then list ways the characters might solve the problem.

Harcourt

Name _____

▶ **Write the correct meaning of each underlined word. Choose from the meanings in the box.**

> **ground:** **a.** the part of the earth that is solid **b.** crushed into small pieces
> **nose:** **a.** the part of the face used for breathing **b.** to push forward gently
> **snapped:** **a.** broke suddenly **b.** spoke sharply
> **started:** **a.** began **b.** moved suddenly from surprise
> **store:** **a.** a place to shop **b.** to keep things in a place for future use
> **windows:** **a.** a computer term **b.** clear parts of a building, made of glass

1. Desmoana <u>started</u> when Encyclopedia accused her of lying.

Started means _____

2. The <u>ground</u> was covered with snow when the children woke up in the morning.

Ground means _____

3. A twig <u>snapped</u> under Encyclopedia's feet as he crept through the woods.

Snapped means _____

4. Encyclopedia <u>started</u> the day with a good breakfast.

Started means _____

5. Encyclopedia used separate <u>windows</u> on his computer screen to divide the information he needed to <u>store</u>.

Windows is _____

and *store* means _____

6. Encyclopedia's dog began to <u>nose</u> the door open.

Nose means _____

7. The suspect <u>snapped</u> at the detective when he asked her a tough question.

Snapped means _____

8. Pablo <u>ground</u> plaster and water into a paste before beginning his art project.

Ground means _____

Name _____

▶ **Write the possessive pronouns that could replace each
group of words below.**

	Before a Noun	**Not Before a Noun**
1. Martha Katz's	_____	_____
2. the townspeople's	_____	_____
3. belonging to me	_____	_____
4. Pablo's	_____	_____
5. owned by Sally and me	_____	_____

▶ **Rewrite each sentence, replacing the
underlined words with possessive pronouns.**

6. Pablo did not ride <u>Pablo's</u> bike to Encyclopedia's house.

_____

7. Pablo and Sally had almost made up <u>Pablo's and Sally's</u> minds.

_____

8. Sally eagerly gave Encyclopedia <u>Sally's</u> opinion.

_____

9. "Yes, that bike is <u>Desmoana's</u>," admitted Desmoana at last.

_____

10. "You and I make a great team, Sally," Encyclopedia said. "The credit for
solving this case is <u>Sally's and Encyclopedia's</u>."

_____

_____

**TRY
THIS!** What are some of your favorite things? Use possessive pronouns to write
five sentences about the items. Include examples of both kinds of
possessive pronouns.

124 Touch a Dream

Name _____

▶ **Read each word. Then write a Spelling Word with the opposite meaning by adding the prefix *un-* or *dis-*.**

1. clean _____

2. like _____

3. happy _____

4. used _____

5. kind _____

6. friendly _____

7. heard _____

8. agree _____

SPELLING WORDS

1. unused
2. dislike
3. unclean
4. unheard
5. disagree
6. disabled
7. unkind
8. unfriendly
9. unable
10. unhappy
11. unsafe
12. disobey

▶ **Write a Spelling Word to complete each sentence.**

9. This intersection is _____.

10. Too many drivers _____ the stop sign.

11. People who use wheelchairs are

   _____ to cross the street here.

12. There are no curb ramps for people

   who are _____.

Handwriting Tip: Take care to hold your pen or pencil properly— about an inch from the point, between the thumb and first finger. Write the Spelling Words below.

13. unkind _____   15. unhappy _____

14. unable _____   16. unsafe _____

Name _____

▶ **Choose a word from the bricks to complete each sentence
below. Fill in one letter per blank. Some words are used twice.**

| thrifty | generous | roguish | rascally | fascinated |

"Notice for House Guests."

1. We serve _ _ _ _ _ _ _ _ portions, so eat all you like.

2. We try to be _ _ _ _ _ _ _, so please do not waste food.

3. If you are _ _ _ _ _ _ _ _ _ _ _ by something you see here,
   please ask about it.

4. The _ _ _ _ _ _ _ _ activity of stealing towels is illegal.

5. _ _ _ _ _ _ _ house guests may not return here.

6. We charge very little, so please be a _ _ _ _ _ _ _ guest.

7. Feel free to leave a _ _ _ _ _ _ _ _ tip at the end of your stay.

8. We are _ _ _ _ _ _ _ _ _ _ by interesting stories, so please
   share any you may have!

▶ **Fill in the blanks below.**

9. Write two Vocabulary Words that are synonyms.

   _____   _____

10. Write two Vocabulary Words that are antonyms.

   _____   _____

TRY THIS! Make a list of rules you think parents should follow, using at least two
Vocabulary Words.

Harcourt

Name _____

▶ Complete the Venn diagram below by telling how the old
woman is different from the two young men. Then tell
how all three characters are the same.

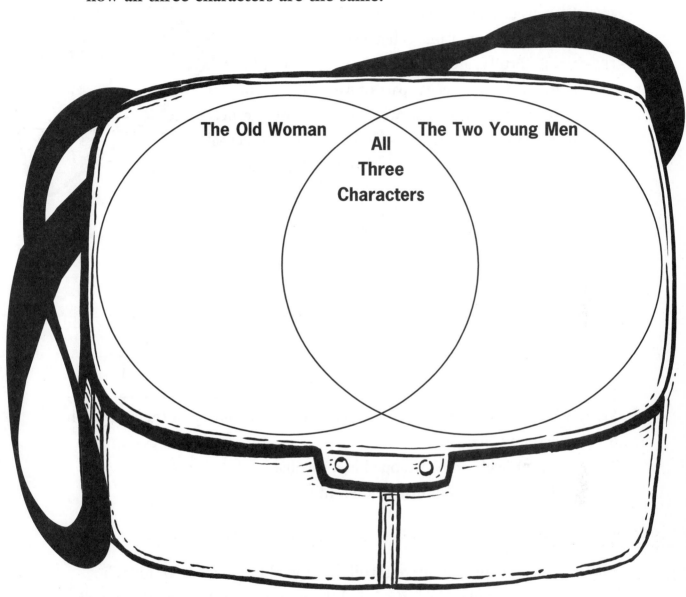

The Old Woman   **All Three Characters**   **The Two Young Men**

▶ Briefly describe how the old woman manages to fool the young men.

_____

_____

_____

_____

Harcourt

Name _____

▶ **Read each paragraph. Then follow the instructions and
answer the questions.**

Wrap them around beans and cheese. Fill them with
chicken or beef. Eat them plain. What are they? Tortillas
(tor-TEE-yuhz)! Tortillas are a flat bread made of corn flour
or wheat flour. They have been a part of Mexican cooking for
hundreds of years. At first tortillas were made of corn kernels that
were boiled in a mixture of water and lime. The boiled kernels were
then ground into flour. The flour was dampened, patted into a pancake,
and baked on a griddle.

1. Write a paraphrase of the last sentence. _____

_____

2. Write a one-sentence summary of the paragraph. _____

_____

_____

3. Write which of these sentences belongs in a good summary of the paragraph.
   a. Tortillas are delicious.
   b. Chicken or beef can be wrapped in a tortilla.
   c. Tortillas can be used in many different ways.

_____

Although some people still make tortillas in the old way, many of today's
tortillas are machine-made. Machines grind the corn or wheat, shape the dough
into discs, and bake it. Sometimes machines even freeze the tortillas so they can
be stored for long periods of time.

4. Write a paraphrase of the first sentence. _____

_____

5. Write a one-sentence summary of the paragraph. _____

_____

Harcourt

▶ **Read the paragraph. Then read each question and choose
the best answer. Mark the letter for that answer.**

If you enjoy eating tamales, thank the native peoples of Mexico. They were making tamales long before Spanish explorers arrived in the Americas. A favorite kind of tamale was made by wrapping a mixture of cornmeal and meat or fish in cornhusks. Tamales can have many different fillings. In some places a sweet version is popular.

1 Which of these sentences belongs in a summary of the paragraph?

  A Mexican restaurants serve tamales.

  B The native peoples ate corn and peppers.

  C Tamales are a tasty food.

  D The first tamales were made by native peoples in Mexico.

2 Which of these is a paraphrase of the first sentence?

  F Tamale fans can thank Mexico's native peoples.

  G If you enjoy eating tamales, thank the native peoples of Mexico.

  H People in Mexico like tamales made with a cornmeal filling.

  J There were people living in Mexico before the Spaniards came.

3 A good summary _____.

  A states the main ideas in a few words

  B is longer than the original

  C restates the original in your own words

  D includes many details

4 "Sweet tamales taste very strange." Why is this *not* a good paraphrase of the last sentence?

  F It is too short.

  G It gives only the main idea.

  H It does not restate the same information.

  J It gives unimportant details.

5 A paraphrase of a paragraph _____.

  A is very long

  B uses other words to restate the information

  C gives only a few details

  D tells only the main idea

Answers

1 Ⓐ Ⓑ Ⓒ Ⓓ

2 Ⓕ Ⓖ Ⓗ Ⓙ

3 Ⓐ Ⓑ Ⓒ Ⓓ

4 Ⓕ Ⓖ Ⓗ Ⓙ

5 Ⓐ Ⓑ Ⓒ Ⓓ

Harcourt

Name _____

In the Days of
King Adobe

Extending
Vocabulary:
Synonyms and
Antonyms

▶ **Write a synonym for each underlined word in the
sentences below. Use the words in the box.**

skinny	interested	stuffed	giving	mean
worst	increases	dishonest	boring	reckless

1. The young men were <u>full</u> after the
   delicious dinner.   _____

2. The old woman was <u>thin</u> from
   lack of food.   _____

3. It is rare to find someone who
   is <u>generous</u> to strangers.   _____

4. The children were <u>fascinated</u> to
   hear the old woman's stories.   _____

5. The young men were <u>cruel</u> to
   steal food from a poor woman.   _____

▶ **Write an antonym for each underlined word in the sentences below.
Use the words in the box.**

6. She was an <u>honest</u> person in that story.   _____

7. He is <u>careful</u> with garden tools.   _____

8. I always manage to pick the <u>best</u>
   piece of ham at Grandma's.   _____

9. He <u>reduces</u> the number of prizes
   we can win each year.   _____

10. The show was so <u>interesting</u> that
    we talked about it for a long time.   _____

Harcourt

Name _____

► **Rewrite each sentence. Replace the blank with the type of adjective in parentheses ( ).**

1. The visitors described the _____ dreams. **(how many?)**

   _____

   _____

2. It was a(n) _____ evening. **(what kind?)**

   _____

   _____

3. The woman cooked _____ meal. **(which one?)**

   _____

   _____

4. Did _____ travelers learn a lesson? **(which ones?)**

   _____

   _____

5. This was quite a(n) _____ adventure. **(what kind?)**

   _____

   _____

► **Rewrite each sentence, using the correct article in parentheses ( ).**

6. **(A, The)** travelers arrived at **(a, the)** old woman's house.

   _____

7. Did they enjoy **(a, an)** exciting meal?

   _____

8. **(An, The)** ham was **(a, an)** big surprise!

   _____

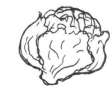

Harcourt

Name _____

▶ **Use the Spelling Words and the clues below to complete the puzzle.**

Across

4. pay back
5. not busy
6. go back
9. not finished
10. consider again
11. containing no fat
12. took the place of

Down

1. say again
2. without stopping
3. not right
7. to make full again
8. read again

SPELLING WORDS

1. *nonstop*
2. *replaced*
3. *inactive*
4. *refill*
5. *incorrect*
6. *rethink*
7. *nonfat*
8. *reread*
9. *retell*
10. *return*
11. *incomplete*
12. *repay*

Handwriting Tip: Use just one overjoining stroke when writing the letter *n*, or it might look like *m*. Write the Spelling Words below.

inactive

13. return _____   15. incorrect _____

14. inactive _____   16. incomplete _____

SCHOOL-HOME CONNECTION With your child, think of three more words that have prefixes or suffixes. Then use the words in sentences.

Harcourt

Name _____

▶ **Write a word from the box to complete each sentence.
Some words will be used twice.**

script	triumphantly	desperately	injustice
repentant	acceptable	discards	circumstances

Blue Grass **(1)** _____ wants to change sad songs

into happy ones. First, he **(2)** _____ any songs
that make him cry. Then, he replaces them with songs that have

happy endings and are **(3)** _____ to him.

With these new **(4)** _____, he declares

(5) _____ to his audience that they will go
home happy when they hear his songs.

But then an offer comes to him to write a sad song for a movie

(6) _____! He knows this movie song would make him

famous. He thinks, "What an **(7)** _____ — to become

famous for writing a sad song!" He **(8)** _____ the movie offer
and continues writing happy songs.

But he worries that he may be **(9)** _____ about this

decision. He is very confused. He **(10)** _____ wants to be a
famous songwriter.

Finally, a friend tells him there are many kinds of beautiful songs. He

knows what to do now under these **(11)** _____. He

(12) _____ writes all kinds of songs that people can enjoy
in different ways.

SCHOOL-HOME CONNECTION Retell a favorite fairy tale or
other story with your child. Change the plot so that the ending is
completely different. Use at least three Vocabulary Words.

Touch a Dream **133**

Harcourt

Name _____

Skill Reminder	summary = main idea and details

paraphrase = the same information stated in other words

▶ **Read the paragraph. Then answer the questions.**

Do you ever play alphabet games and need a word that begins with *z*? If you're tired of *zoo* and *zebra*, next time try *zither*. A zither is a stringed musical instrument. It looks a little bit like a harp that's lying down. Zithers have anywhere from 29 to 42 strings. To play, you pluck the strings with the fingers of both hands. Many hundreds of years ago, the Greeks played an instrument called a *cithara*. The zither probably developed from the cithara. Zithers aren't very common anymore, but they were popular in the United States during the 1800s.

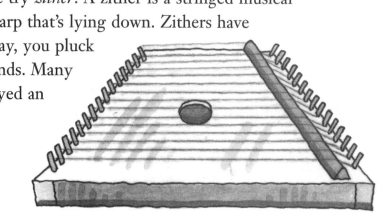

1. Write a short summary of the paragraph.

_____

_____

_____

_____

_____

2. Write a paraphrase of the last sentence of the paragraph.

_____

_____

_____

TRY THIS! Make a list of the events that took place as you came to school today. Then write a one-sentence summary based on your list.

Harcourt

▶ Before you read, fill in the prediction chart by writing what you think will happen. After you read, write what actually happens.

What I Predict Will Happen	What Actually Happens

▶ Why does Red Writing Hood wish to change the fairy tales and nursery rhymes? Think about the kind of person she is.

_____

_____

_____

Name _____

▶ **Write the letter of a good strategy to use from the box to find the meaning of each underlined word. Then write the meaning of the word from the choices given.**

A. Look for a prefix or a suffix.

B. Think about the meaning of the base word.

C. See if the word is a compound word.

Have you read the fairy tale about the elves who helped the shoemaker?

1. Strategy: _____

2. *Shoemaker* means _____.

    a kind of shoe   **making tools**   **a person who makes shoes**

The man was so poor that it was impossible for him to buy leather for more shoes.

3. Strategy: _____

4. *Impossible* means _____.

    possible   **not possible**   **very likely**

One morning, to his astonishment, he found a perfectly made pair of shoes. He had no idea who his mysterious helpers were.

5. Strategy: _____

6. *Mysterious* means _____.

    full of mystery   **without mystery**   **too much mystery**

Imagine his disbelief when he discovered the elves at work!

7. Strategy: _____

8. *Disbelief* means _____.

    full of belief   **believable**   **the opposite of belief**

SCHOOL-HOME CONNECTION With your child, start a collection of long words that you hear or see in print. Talk about each word's pronunciation and meaning.

Harcourt

Name _____

▶ **Rewrite each sentence, using the correct form of the adjective in parentheses ( ).**

1. Red whistled a _____ tune. **(joyful)**

   _____

2. It was a _____ tune than the one she whistled yesterday. **(happy)**

   _____

3. In fact, it was the _____ tune she had whistled all week. **(nice)**

   _____

4. The wolf was looking forward to a _____ treat. **(tasty)**

   _____

5. "These are the _____ berries I've ever had," he grinned. **(fine)**

   _____

6. "Strawberries are _____ than blueberries," he declared. **(sweet)**

   _____

▶ **Complete each sentence by writing the correct form of *good* in the blank.**

7. Making the wolf a ballet dancer

   was _____ than having him visit Grandma's house.

8. Miss Muffet thought the new

   ending was the _____ she had heard.

TRY THIS! Imagine that your three favorite story characters could meet. Write a conversation they might have. Use several adjectives that compare. Exchange conversations with a classmate, and discuss the adjectives you used.

Harcourt

Name _____

▶ **Write the Spelling Word that means the opposite of each word or phrase.**

1. with difficulty _____

2. sadly _____

3. lighter _____

4. prettiest _____

5. hugest _____

6. later _____

SPELLING WORDS

1. *families*
2. *worried*
3. *ugliest*
4. *funnier*
5. *happily*
6. *easily*
7. *heavier*
8. *earlier*
9. *tiniest*
10. *supplied*
11. *luckily*
12. *relied*

▶ **Write a Spelling Word to complete each sentence.**

Five **(7)** _____ met at the park.

Each family **(8)** _____ some food.

Dad and I **(9)** _____ that it might rain.

Mom **(10)** _____ on the weather report.

(11) _____, the weather report was correct and it didn't rain. We all told funny stories.

My story was **(12)** _____ than all the others.

Stories

Handwriting Tip: When you write the letter combination *lie*, be sure that only the *l* reaches the top writing line. Write the Spelling Words below.

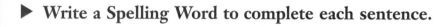

earlier

13. families _____   15. earlier _____

14. ugliest _____   16. supplied _____

Harcourt

▶ **Write a word from the box to complete each analogy.**

decreed	famine	implored	trickle	plentifully

1. *Singer* is to *chanted* as *beggar* is to _____.

2. *Reward* is to *punishment* as *feast* is to _____.

3. *Teacher* is to *instructed* as *king* is to _____.

4. *Enormous* is to *tiny* as *flood* is to _____.

5. *Quick* is to *quickly* as *plentiful* is to _____.

▶ **Write the word that matches each clue.**

6. This happens when there's no food. _____

7. A judge did this. _____

8. It's how generous people give gifts. _____

9. Someone in need did this. _____

10. It's in a mostly dried-up stream. _____

 TRY THIS! Make up your own folktale about a grain of rice. Include at least two Vocabulary Words.

Harcourt

Name _____

▶ Complete the sequence chart below by writing important story events in the boxes.

Important Events During Rani's Thirty Days

Date	Event
first day	
second day	
ninth day	
twentieth day	
twenty-fourth day	
twenty-ninth day	
thirtieth day	

▶ Use the information in your time line to figure out how many grains of rice Rani would have received on the thirty-second day. Explain how you got your answer.

_____

_____

_____

Harcourt

Name _____

▶ **On the lines, write the answers to the questions.**

More than half of India's land is used for farming. Its main products are rice, wheat, sugarcane, tea, and cotton. Rice is the main food eaten by much of the population.

1. Is the paragraph objective or subjective? _____

2. How can you tell? _____

_____

Last September, I spent seven days in New Delhi, India. It poured rain on all seven days. I think that it must rain every day in India.

3. Is the paragraph objective or subjective? _____

4. How can you tell? _____

_____

5. The author says that it must rain every day in India. Is this conclusion valid?

Explain. _____

_____

The national soccer team lost to Brazil yesterday by the score of 3–2. We have a terrible team this year. We have already lost three games.

6. Is the paragraph objective or subjective? _____

7. How can you tell? _____

_____

Brazil, a top-ranked team, barely outscored our national soccer team yesterday by the score of 3–2. We can be proud of our team, which has won eight games this year while losing only three.

8. Is the paragraph objective or subjective? Explain. _____

_____

TRY THIS! Write a paragraph about a real or imaginary sports event. Choose words so the home team seems to be either a good or bad team.

Harcourt

Name _____

▶ **Write each underlined word beside the correct definition below.**

Rick's skin was very <u>fair</u>, so he put on a lot of sunblock.

Mrs. Morse kept the <u>deed</u> to her land locked in a safe.

Leah received a <u>reward</u> for finding the lost cat.

Martha could <u>double</u> her money if she worked all summer.

The ruler kept a huge <u>store</u> of rice hidden away.

The girl wasn't sure her <u>scheme</u> would work.

The ruler <u>declared</u> that all the people could share the wealth.

When the others <u>barred</u> the girl from entering the palace, the ruler let her in.

The ruler <u>scrutinized</u> the plan and decided it would work.

The girl was <u>overjoyed</u>, so she celebrated.

1. _____ looked over carefully

2. _____ money given for the return of lost property

3. _____ plan

4. _____ a legal document

5. _____ a supply of things put away for later use

6. _____ very happy

7. _____ stated

8. _____ light-colored

9. _____ stopped

10. _____ make twice as much

SCHOOL-HOME CONNECTION Help your child find three new words in a dictionary. Then help him or her use the new words in sentences.

Harcourt

Name _____

▶ **Underline the complete predicate in each sentence, and circle the verb. On the line, write *action* or *being* to identify the verb.**

1. China and India are the biggest producers of rice in the world. _____

2. Farmers in Arkansas, California, Texas, and Louisiana grow a lot of rice, too. _____

3. Rice plants thrive in 4 to 8 inches of water. _____

4. Actually, rice is the fruit of a type of grass. _____

5. Harvesters remove rice grains from the plant. _____

6. At the mill, workers process the rice. _____

▶ **Underline the verb or verb group in each sentence. Then write a new sentence using the verb or verb group you underlined.**

7. Bran, a thin brown skin, covers rice. _____

   _____

8. Brown rice has many vitamins and minerals. _____

   _____

9. The bran is removed at the mill. _____

   _____

10. The kernels are polished for white rice. _____

   _____

TRY THIS! Rani used mathematics to feed the people. Write five sentences about ways people use mathematics. Underline the verbs in your sentences.

Name _____

▶ **Write the Spelling Word that matches each clue.**

1. answer   _____

2. purpose   _____

3. more than enough   _____

4. sorrow   _____

5. silence   _____

SPELLING WORDS
1. addition
2. sadness
3. lovable
4. endless
5. handful
6. plentiful
7. breathless
8. happiness
9. solution
10. careful
11. function
12. stillness

▶ **Add a suffix to the underlined word to write a Spelling Word.**

6. Put your <u>hand</u> into the jar and

   grab a _____ of rice.

7. We all <u>love</u> the new puppy. Boots is a

   _____ little dog.

8. I thought that movie would never <u>end</u>.

   It seemed _____!

9. Do you like to <u>add</u>? Yes, _____ is
   my favorite part of math.

10. Take <u>care</u> when you ride your bike. It's important

    to be _____ on the road.

11. Jed grew short of <u>breath</u> as he ran. He was _____.

12. Habib felt so <u>happy</u>! His _____ showed in his wide grin.

Handwriting Tip: Keep your letter strokes smooth and steady. Do not go over your strokes again. Write the Spelling Words below.

13. addition _____

14. sadness _____

15. endless _____

16. handful _____

Harcourt

Name _____

▶ **Write a word from the water to best complete each sentence.**
  Use some words twice.

ventilate   billowing   brigade
curfew   dedication   loyalty   flammable

Tony has been thinking about firefighting as a career because he likes
helping people. He knows that firefighting demands commitment and

(1) _____. By nature he is a true friend, and he has shown his

(2) _____ by helping his friends solve their problems. Tony
decided the best way to find out if he would like to be a firefighter would be
to spend some time at his local fire station. But since his parents have set a

(3) _____ for him, he would not be able to stay past 8:00 P.M.
When Tony arrived, the firefighters explained how the first firefighting

(4) _____ had formed long ago. They told him about the many

new inventions, such as clothing that is not **(5)** _____, that help
firefighters stay safe.

Tony told the firefighters that he knew smoke was dangerous. He had learned
that he should crawl on his knees if caught in a fire. Since the smoke would be

(6) _____ upward, the cleanest air would be near the floor.
The firefighters said this is why they wear breathing masks. They have to

(7) _____ their lungs so they can stand up to work.
The firefighters also reminded Tony about outdoor fires and how quickly
they can spread in a forest because wood is very

(8) _____. Tony didn't
want to leave but knew the time of his

(9) _____ was getting near.

He was more impressed than ever with firefighters' **(10)** _____

and **(11)** _____ to their jobs and to helping the community.

SCHOOL-HOME CONNECTION Talk with your child about fire-
safety rules to observe both inside and outside your home. Use
some Vocabulary Words.

Harcourt

Skill Reminder **Manage your time. Skip questions you don't know.**

▶ Write the test-taking strategies from the box in the order that they should be followed.

Return to questions I skipped.	**Check my answers.**
Look over the whole test.	**Answer questions I know first.**
Read directions carefully.	

1. First: _____

2. Next: _____

3. Then: _____

4. Then: _____

5. Last: _____

▶ Write the answer to the question from the choices below. Then write the letters of the strategies you used.

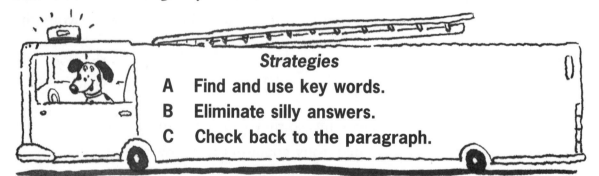

Strategies
A Find and use key words.
B Eliminate silly answers.
C Check back to the paragraph.

Dalmatians are spotted dogs that have been popular with fire departments for over 100 years. These dogs were able to run along with horse-drawn fire engines without getting kicked accidentally by the horses. Even when motorized fire trucks came along, Dalmatians stayed on as fire department mascots.

6. What special ability do Dalmatians have?

_____

fighting fires   **running behind horses without getting kicked**

Harcourt

▶ **Fill in the first two columns of the K-W-L chart. Then use information from the story to fill in the last column.**

What I <u>K</u>now	What I <u>W</u>ant to Know	What I <u>L</u>earned

▶ **Write a one-sentence summary of the whole selection.**

_____

_____

Name _____

▶ **Read the paragraph. Then write three facts from the paragraph on the top fire truck and three opinions from the paragraph on the bottom fire truck.**

A student who is studying to be an emergency medical technician, or EMT, in Dallas must work a 24-hour shift at a fire station. The students go with firefighters who answer calls for medical help. This is the most exciting part of EMT training. It's a real thrill to ride on the ambulance through the city streets! Sometimes they give first aid to someone who is injured. Providing emergency medical care is a hard job.

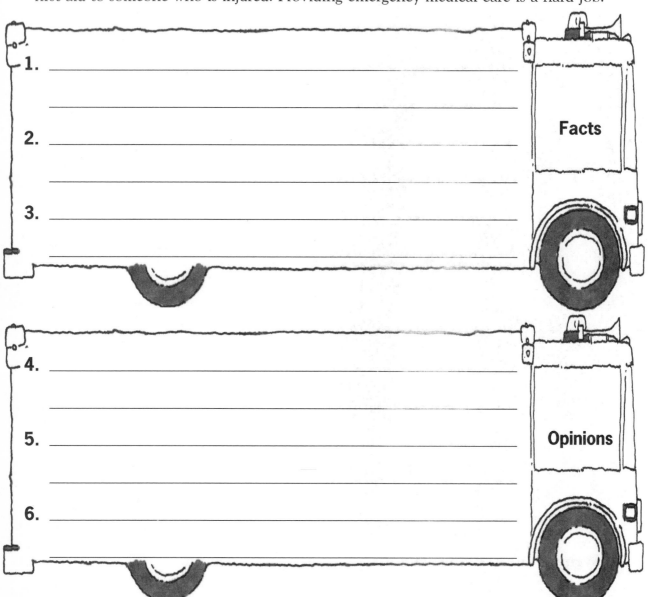

1. _____

2. _____

3. _____

Facts

4. _____

5. _____

6. _____

Opinions

TRY THIS! Look at the illustration of the firefighter's turnout gear in "Fire!" Write your opinion of how it would feel to wear that gear.

Harcourt

▶ **Read the passage. Then read each question and decide which is the best answer. Mark the letter for that answer.**

Some people like to work for no money at all! Every summer many students do volunteer work. Some work in hospitals. The most rewarding job there is working with children. Volunteers read to children and play with them. Volunteers do other jobs, too, such as helping in the hospital offices. Hospital volunteer work is a good way to spend the summer. It is not boring at all.

There are many volunteer organizations. Working for your community is a wonderful job. Everyone should try it. You can ask your local hospital for an application. Or you can volunteer at another place. You won't be sorry.

1 Which sentence is an opinion?

A Some people like to work for no money at all!

B Every summer many students do volunteer work.

C Some work in hospitals.

D Hospital volunteer work is a good way to spend the summer.

2 Which sentence is a fact?

F The most rewarding job is working with children.

G Volunteers read to children and play with them.

H Hospital volunteer work is a good way to spend the summer.

J It is not boring at all.

3 Which sentence is an opinion?

A There are many volunteer organizations.

B Everyone should try it.

C You can ask your local hospital for an application.

D Or you can volunteer at another place.

4 Which sentence is a fact?

F Working for your community is a wonderful job.

G Everyone should try it.

H You can ask your local hospital for an application.

J You won't be sorry.

Answers

1 Ⓐ Ⓑ Ⓒ Ⓓ

2 Ⓕ Ⓖ Ⓗ Ⓙ

3 Ⓐ Ⓑ Ⓒ Ⓓ

4 Ⓕ Ⓖ Ⓗ Ⓙ

Harcourt

Name _____

▶ Use the book cover, table of contents, glossary, and index
to answer the questions on the next page.

Fighting the Blaze
by James and Sandra Boyd

**True Stories of Firefighters
in All 50 States**

Table of Contents

Glossary

alarm: a bell or siren used to give a
   warning
brigade: a group of people organized
   for a certain purpose
paramedic units: groups that give
   emergency first aid on the scene
pumper: a truck that carries a pump
   and hoses for spraying water on a
   fire
smoke detector: a device that
   sounds an alarm if there is smoke
   in a room

Index

Harcourt

GO ON

Name _____

▶ **Write your answer to each question. Then write the name of the book part where you found each answer.**

1. What is the title of the book? _____

Book part: _____

2. How many chapters does the book have? _____

Book part: _____

3. On what page does the third chapter begin? _____

Book part: _____

4. What is a *pumper*? _____

Book part: _____

5. What page mentions Little Rock, Arkansas? _____

Book part: _____

6. Which pages mention an airport crash truck? _____

Book part: _____

7. Who are the authors of the book? _____

Book part: _____

8. Which chapter has stories about pets? _____

Book part: _____

9. What are *paramedic units*? _____

_____

Book part: _____

10. Which cities in California are mentioned? _____

Book part: _____

Name _____

▶ **Write a word from the list to complete each sentence.**

worker   a call into the station, requiring the fire
    truck and firefighters to go out
bunker   type of pants tucked into rubber boots
overhaul   to remove cinders and anything that
    might burn and to soak the area with water
rekindle   to restart
dispatch   the switchboard that takes incoming calls
turnout   firefighting gear
knocked down   completely put out
back-stepper   an old-fashioned term for *firefighter*

1. The crew jumped on the truck and headed out

    when the _____ came in.

2. An urgent phone call came in to the _____ operator.

3. Tim found an old newspaper picture of a _____
    putting out a fire.

4. It took five hours, but finally the fire was _____.

5. The crew grabbed all of their _____ before jumping
    on the fire truck.

6. They stayed behind at the scene of the fire to make sure the fire did not

    _____.

7. He always sets out his _____ pants before going to sleep
    at the fire station.

8. The chief made every person on the crew work to carefully

    _____ the fire scene.

TRY THIS!   Read in a reference book about another interesting profession. Research
the special terms used in that profession.

Harcourt

Name _____

▶ **Underline the main verb. Circle the helping verb.**

1. The children have opened the hydrant.

2. Water is pouring all over the ground.

3. Their game could prove dangerous.

4. Perhaps the water will dry up.

5. Then any fire would cause
   great damage.

▶ **Complete each sentence. Use a verb from the box. Then circle the helping verb.**

| take | deserve | extinguished | relaxing | answer |

6. The firefighters were _____.

7. They had _____ a fire early that morning.

8. They do _____ a break now.

9. One firefighter will _____ the phones.

10. The rest should _____ a nap.

TRY THIS! On a separate sheet of paper, write five sentences about fighting fires. Use one of these helping verbs in each sentence: *were could does has will*

Harcourt

Name _____

▶ **Write the Spelling Word that names each picture.**

1. _____

3. _____

2. _____

4. _____

SPELLING WORDS
1. doctor
2. dollar
3. power
4. sugar
5. corner
6. collar
7. danger
8. ladder
9. labor
10. cellar
11. other
12. motor

▶ **The letters of the underlined words are mixed up. Write the correct Spelling Words on the lines.**

5. The <u>rtoom</u> of the fire engine is huge. _____

6. The firefighters drink coffee with <u>agusr</u> in it for energy. _____

7. Smoke is coming from the <u>clrale</u>. _____

8. The firefighters and a <u>rooctd</u> are on the way. _____

9. Is there any <u>radnge</u> of an explosion? _____

10. It will take hard <u>boarl</u> to break down that cellar door. _____

11. Water shoots from a fire hose with tremendous <u>worep</u>. _____

12. Should we call for any <u>hotre</u> kinds of help? _____

Handwriting Tip: When you connect the vowels *a*, *o*, and *e* to *r*, make sure the *r* does not look like an *i*. Write the Spelling Words below.

corner

13. sugar _____

15. labor _____

14. corner _____

16. doctor _____

Harcourt

Name _____

▶ **Write the word from the box that matches each clue. The
message in the shaded area of the answers tells you what
a person may become on an important day.**

apologized	obliged	certificate	examiner
petitioners	resounded	enrich	

1. an official document   _ _ _ _ _ _ _ _ _ _ _

2. one who gives a test   _ _ _ _ _ _ _ _

3. people asking for something   _ _ _ _ _ _ _ _ _ _ _

4. to make better   _ _ _ _ _ _

5. said "I'm sorry"   _ _ _ _ _ _ _ _ _ _

6. did what was wanted   _ _ _ _ _ _ _

7. echoed   _ _ _ _ _ _ _ _ _

▶ **Write the word that answers each riddle.**

8. I am an important piece of paper.
    What am I?   _____

9. We are requesting something.
    Who are we?   _____

10. I give exams.
    Who am I?   _____

I pledge allegiance to the flag . . .

TRY THIS! Write a paragraph telling what country your family came from and when. Use at least three Vocabulary Words.

Touch a Dream **155**

Harcourt

Name _____

> **Skill Reminder**   Book Cover — title, author; Table of
> Contents — chapter titles and page number where each
> chapter begins; Glossary — definitions of words;
> Index — page numbers of topics

▶ Read each question and the names of the book parts. Then write the name
of the book part where you could find the answer to each question.

| Book Cover | Table of Contents | Glossary | Index |

1. Who wrote the book? _____

2. What is the title of the first chapter? _____

3. On what page is Brooklyn mentioned? _____

4. What does the word *Constitution* mean? _____

5. On what page does the chapter "How
   to Become a Citizen" begin? _____

6. Which pages tell about immigration? _____

7. How many chapters does the book have? _____

8. What is a *borough*? _____

9. What pages tell about the Pledge of
   Allegiance? _____

10. What is the title of the book? _____

TRY THIS!   Look at several different magazines in your classroom and compare the
tables of contents. Do they all give the same information? In what ways are
they different?

156   Touch a Dream

Harcourt

Name _____

Skill Reminder	Fact — can be supported by evidence

Opinion — states a belief, judgment, or feeling

▶ **Write *fact* or *opinion* beside each sentence.**

1. One of the best things about visiting New York City is a trip

to Ellis Island. _____

2. This is the place where more than 12 million immigrants entered the

United States between 1892 and 1954. _____

3. The first one to pass through Ellis Island was a 15-year-old

Irish girl named Annie Moore. _____

4. How exciting it must have been to

arrive in America! _____

5. Annie arrived on the steamship *Nevada*

on January 1, 1892. _____

6. She came with her two younger brothers. _____

7. They were met by their parents, who had come to New York three years

before. _____

8. Annie was the bravest girl alive. _____

9. She must have truly wanted to be an American. _____

10. Today there is a bronze statue of Annie on the second floor of the Ellis

Island Immigration Museum. _____

Write a paragraph about someone you admire. Include both facts and
opinions. Label the facts *F* and the opinions *O*.

Harcourt

Name _____

▶ As you read, start to fill in the prediction web. After you
read, write what actually happens.

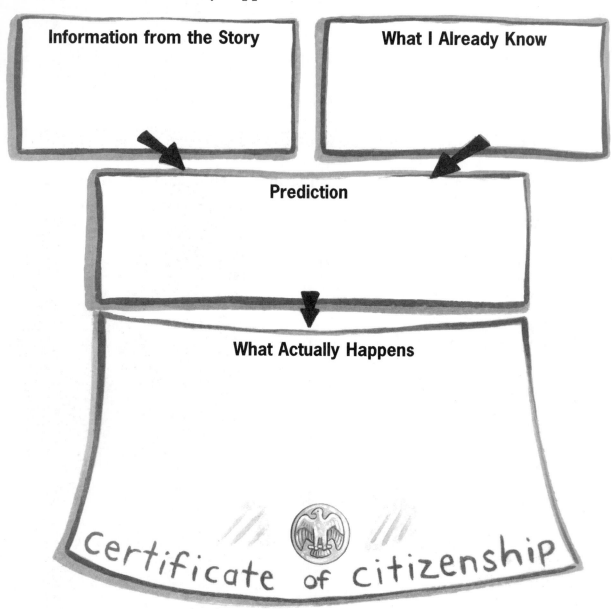

Information from the Story

What I Already Know

Prediction

What Actually Happens

certificate of citizenship

▶ Explain why all the characters refer to the day as "a very important day."
What makes it so important to them?

_____

_____

_____

_____

Harcourt

▶ **Read the paragraph. Then write *valid* or *invalid* beside each generalization.**

When Hans arrived in the United States in 1907, he didn't speak English. At Ellis Island he stood in line with hundreds of other immigrants, waiting for permission to enter the country. How long the line was! How tired Hans felt after his long journey from Germany with his family! Hans and the others had to be examined by a doctor right away. If the doctor found any medical problems, then the immigrant had to be examined again by other doctors. Hans was very nervous. Sick children over the age of 12 could not leave Ellis Island to enter the United States. They had to go back across the ocean alone. Their parents and family did not return with them. Hans had just had his twelfth birthday. He hoped the doctor wouldn't notice his little cough.

Generalization	Valid or Invalid
1. Immigrants do not speak English.	_____
2. Immigrants have illnesses.	_____
3. Some immigrants weren't allowed to enter the United States.	_____
4. Sometimes immigrant children were separated from their parents.	_____
5. All immigrants were nervous.	_____
6. Some immigrants came from Germany.	_____
7. Doctors worked at Ellis Island.	_____
8. Doctors were always cruel to the immigrants.	_____
9. Children were always separated from their parents.	_____
10. Sometimes families immigrated together.	_____

Harcourt

Name _____

▶ Homographs are words that are spelled the same but have
different meanings and, often, different pronunciations.
Write the word from the box that can replace both underlined
words in the sentence.

| desert | suspect | dove | extract |
| minute | records | wind | produce |

1. The airplane swooped in order to miss the bird.   _____

2. The breeze was so strong that Mark could
   not tighten the spring of the clock in the tower.   _____

3. Lisa would not leave her friend Jan in the
   hot, dry, sandy area.   _____

4. We could not pull out the part of the plant that
   is used to make vanilla concentrate.   _____

5. It took only sixty seconds to dig down to the
   tiny roots of the plant.   _____

6. The man writes down facts that become part of
   historical documents.   _____

7. I am beginning to think it likely that the
   person under suspicion is guilty.   _____

8. My garden can grow a large amount of
   fruits and vegetables if I use a special fertilizer.   _____

TRY THIS! List three other words that can be used in two ways. For each word, write
a sentence that uses it with both meanings.

Harcourt

Name _____

▶ **Underline the verb. Tell what kind of verb it is. Write**
action **or** *linking***.**

1. Citizens say the Pledge of Allegiance.   _____

2. "I pledge allegiance to the flag."   _____

3. The Pledge is an oath of loyalty.   _____

4. It promises devotion to the U.S.A.   _____

5. Citizens are proud of their country.   _____

6. They gladly share in the ceremony.   _____

7. The American flag is overhead.   _____

8. It commands everyone's attention.   _____

▶ **Complete each sentence with the kind of verb in parentheses ( ).**

9. Fatima _____
one hand on her heart. **(action)**

10. She _____ very
happy today. **(linking)**

11. Mr. Kao _____
at his new flag. **(action)**

12. He _____
now an American. **(linking)**

Harcourt

SCHOOL-HOME CONNECTION Talk with your child about what being
a citizen means to him or her. With your child, write three sentences
that tell your family's ideas. Underline the verb in each sentence.

Name _____

▶ **Read the following paragraphs. Find and circle the twelve misspelled words. Then write each word correctly on the lines.**

Jorge turned the handal and opened the door. He took a finle look around. The room was quite ushuel. Above the bed hung a singal picture he had painted. It was a jungal scene with a large animle.

Jorge walked over to his tabel. He picked up a bottal of soda and started to read his diary, the record of his personel thoughts. Then he opened an old book and looked at an exampal of his earliest handwriting.

He couldn't believe his trip was an aktual event. Was it possibel that he was going to move to another country?

	SPELLING WORDS
	1. table
	2. final
	3. handle
	4. personal
	5. animal
	6. usual
	7. jungle
	8. actual
	9. example
	10. bottle
	11. possible
	12. single

1. _____ 7. _____

2. _____ 8. _____

3. _____ 9. _____

4. _____ 10. _____

5. _____ 11. _____

6. _____ 12. _____

Handwriting Tip: Be sure all letters slant in the same direction. Write the Spelling Words below.

final

13. handle _____ 15. example _____

14. actual _____ 16. bottle _____

Harcourt

Name _____

▶ **Write a word from the box to complete each sentence.**

| local | attic | gymnasium | installed | trolley | sweltering |

1. We went upstairs to the _____ to find our old roller skates.

2. The _____ weather station didn't say how hot it would be today.

3. The house was _____, and I had to turn on the fan.

4. We ordered an air conditioner, but it hasn't been _____ yet.

5. Later, when it cools off, I'm going to the _____ to work out.

6. When I leave, I'll ride the _____ downtown.

▶ **Write the Vocabulary Word that best fits with each pair of words or phrases below.**

7. top floor   storage space

_____

8. put in   fixed in place

_____

9. neighborhood   town

_____

10. bus   train

_____

11. hot   humid

_____

12. sports   arena

_____

▶ **Write the Vocabulary Word that means the *opposite* of each clue below.**

13. cold _____   15. worldwide _____

14. taken out _____   16. cellar _____

TRY THIS! Describe the houses or apartments in your neighborhood. Use at least three Vocabulary Words.

Harcourt

Name _____

▶ As you read "House, House," fill in the Venn diagram to describe the city of Hatfield, then and now.

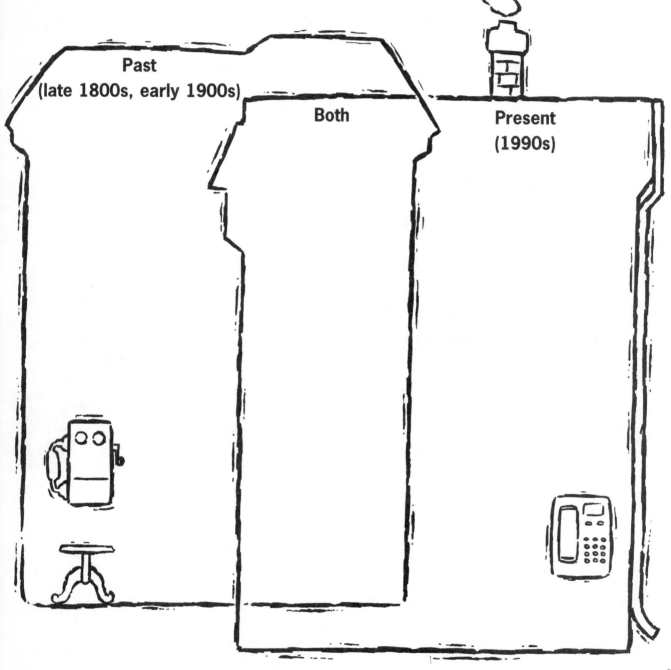

Past
(late 1800s, early 1900s)

Both

Present
(1990s)

▶ As you look at the houses and their surroundings in this selection, describe the changes you see.

_____

_____

_____

Harcourt

Name _____

▶ **Read each paragraph and answer the questions. Choose from the words or phrases below.**

Everyone should support the mayor's efforts to have a citywide cleanup day this spring. We can pick up trash and cut the grass in our park. The wooden play area there needs a coat of paint. The fence needs to be repaired. Some of these projects cost money, but it will be money well spent. A clean, neat park is important. Let's show our pride and clean up our park and our city!

1. The author wants to _____ readers.
   entertain   **inform**   **persuade**

2. The author thinks that cleanup day is a _____ idea.
   good   **bad**   **strange**

3. Probably this author thinks that people should _____

   _____.

   spend more money on parks   **try to save money**   **do nothing**

Having a citywide cleanup day is not a good idea. Much of the painting and other work that our park needs can be paid for by private donations. We should not spend the city's money this way. The money should be spent on street repair instead. Our city's streets are a disgrace. They are bumpy, and some of the holes are large enough to be dangerous. Smooth streets are important for the comfort and safety of everyone in our city.

4. The author wants to _____ readers.
   entertain   **inform**   **persuade**

5. The author believes that a cleanup day is a _____ idea.
   good   **bad**   **strange**

6. The author probably thinks that _____.
   the parks are clean enough   **safety is an issue**   **cities are clean**

TRY THIS! Look back at the selection "Fire!" Write what you think is the author's point of view about firefighting. List the details that help you know this.

Name _____

▶ **Read the paragraph. Then choose the answer that best completes each sentence. Mark the letter for that answer.**

Farm families did not have an easy life in the 1920s. Everyone worked, even the children. Older children worked with the farmhands in the fields, and younger children had chores to do around the house. There was little time for play, and many families had no money for anything more than food and clothing. Days began early, with farm chores to do even before the sun rose. Long days of struggle, trying to raise a large enough crop to support the family, were tiring and not always rewarding.

1 This author probably _____.

  A would like to have lived in the country in the 1920s

  B is glad not to be living on a farm in the 1920s

  C enjoys farm chores

  D would have liked to be a farmer

2 The author's purpose is probably to _____.

  F entertain

  G persuade

  H entertain and to persuade

  J inform

3 The author probably wants readers to _____.

  A forget all about life long ago

  B move to the country

  C appreciate farm families who lived hard lives

  D learn how to grow crops

4 The author would probably agree that _____.

  F farm life was great fun

  G farm life was hard and uncomfortable

  H more people should live on farms

  J life was better in the 1920s than it is now.

5 The author's perspective may depend on _____.

  A whether he has ever lived on a farm

  B where he went on vacation

  C where his ancestors came from

  D how big his family is

Answers
1 Ⓐ Ⓑ Ⓒ Ⓓ
2 Ⓕ Ⓖ Ⓗ Ⓙ
3 Ⓐ Ⓑ Ⓒ Ⓓ
4 Ⓕ Ⓖ Ⓗ Ⓙ
5 Ⓐ Ⓑ Ⓒ Ⓓ

Harcourt

Name _____

▶ **Write the best reference source for finding each answer. Choose from the sources shown below.**

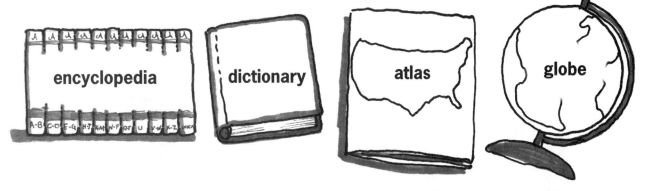

encyclopedia   dictionary   atlas   globe

1. What interstate highways pass through Houston, Texas?

_____

2. What is the correct pronunciation of the word *literacy*?

_____

3. Which South American countries are north of the equator?

_____

4. Where were the first public libraries built?

_____

5. For what work is Horace Mann best known?

_____

6. What does the word *bandwagon* mean?

_____

7. What place is on the exact opposite part of the earth from where you live?

_____

8. How far is it from Dallas to New Orleans?

_____

9. What are the main crops grown in Oklahoma?

_____

10. What is the origin of the word *boondoggle*?

_____

Name _____

▶ **Help Darcy complete her report on national parks.**
Write the entry word or words she should look up in an encyclopedia to
find the information she needs.

1. What did President Theodore Roosevelt do about national parks?

_____

2. Where is Yellowstone National Park located?

_____

3. How is a canyon formed?

_____

4. What is the country's largest national park?

_____

5. Who was John Muir?

_____

6. What are some tips for good photography in national parks?

_____

7. How deep is the Grand Canyon?

_____

8. What was Denali National Park called in the past?

_____

9. Who first explored Carlsbad Caverns?

_____

10. Who built the cliff dwellings at Mesa Verde National Park?

_____

Harcourt

TRY
THIS! Read a magazine article or a nonfiction selection in a book. Make a list of
questions you have about the topic. Beside each, write the entry word or
words you would look up in an encyclopedia to find the answer.

Name _____

▶ **Rewrite these sentences by using the correct present-tense form of the word in parentheses ( ).**

1. The street **(is, was)** lined with beautiful trees.

_____

2. This house is so big that it **(look, looks)** like a mansion.

_____

3. All the houses **(has, have)** large front yards.

_____

4. He **(go, goes)** to the school down the street.

_____

▶ **Write the present-tense form of the verb in parentheses ( ) to complete each sentence.**

5. The small car _____ the garage look huge. **(make)**

6. New cars _____ a lot of money. **(cost)**

7. The dog _____ the boy on their way home. **(pass)**

8. The boy _____ to get on the porch first. **(hurry)**

9. Telephone lines _____ through the community. **(run)**

10. We will need help when we _____ our new house. **(build)**

11. The writer _____ hard at her craft. **(work)**

12. The photographer _____ to take good pictures. **(try)**

TRY THIS! Using only present-tense verbs, write a paragraph describing what you see on your way to school. Then rewrite the paragraph by using the plural subject we.

Harcourt

Name _____

▶ **Write the Spelling Word that fits each clue.**

1. load   _____

2. summer   _____

3. rhymes with *Steven*   _____

4. having to do with cities   _____

5. cause   _____

6. person   _____

SPELLINGWORDS
1. woman
2. even
3. urban
4. seven
5. kitchen
6. reason
7. human
8. season
9. burden
10. wagon
11. oven
12. dragon

▶ **Write the Spelling Word that names each picture.**

7. _____

10. _____

8. _____

11. _____

9. _____

12. _____

Handwriting Tip: When you write the letter combination *on*, take care to keep the joining stroke high. Otherwise, the letters may look like *an*. Write the Spelling Words below.

13. reason _____   **15.** wagon _____

14. season _____   **16.** dragon _____

Harcourt

Name _____

▶ **Write words from the box to replace the underlined words.**

sulkily	indifferent	protruded	loathe
undoubtedly	heartily	certainty	

I had thought that I was going to hate **(1)** _____ Camp

Miller School. Was I wrong! I frowned angrily **(2)** _____

all the way there on my first day. But Miss Peterson was so nice! She is surely

(3) _____ the best teacher in all the camp schools. I no

longer felt disinterested **(4)** _____ about school. My teacher

greeted me in a warm and friendly way **(5)** _____ .

I now feel with sureness **(6)** _____ that I will like

the school after all. The pouting lower lip that once pushed out

(7) _____ from my face has curved into a smile!

▶ **Use each pair of words in one sentence.**

8. indifferent   heartily

_____

_____

9. sulkily   loathe

_____

_____

10. undoubtedly   indifferent

_____

Write about yourself on the first day of a new school year. Tell what
happened and how you felt about it. Use at least three Vocabulary Words.

Harcourt

Name _____

| **Skill Reminder** | purpose = entertain, inform, or persuade |
| | perspective = opinions or attitude |

▶ **Read each paragraph. Then write your answer from the choices of words or phrases to complete each sentence.**

Rafael's Report

The horned toad is an animal that nobody could possibly want to touch. It looks scary, with horns on its head and sharp spines all over its body. It has a mean glare when it looks at someone who has disturbed it. If you see a horned toad, leave it alone!

1. Rafael's main purpose is to

_____.

entertain   inform   persuade

2. Rafael probably _____

_____.

likes horned toads
is afraid of horned toads
knows a lot about lizards

3. Rafael would probably agree that strange-looking creatures

_____.

can be helpful
are actually beautiful
should be left alone

Robert's Report

The horned toad is a harmless little creature that is often misunderstood. It may look a little scary with its sharp spines, but it does no harm. The spines are just to protect it from enemies. Don't let its mean glare fool you. The horned toad won't hurt you at all.

4. Robert's main purpose is to

_____.

entertain   inform   persuade

5. Robert probably _____

_____.

likes only pretty creatures
doesn't judge creatures by looks
thinks all lizards are ugly

6. Robert would probably agree that

_____.

scary-looking creatures are bad
lizards are not helpful to humans
looks can fool you

TRY THIS! Think about an insect or other creature that looks a little scary. Do you like the creature or not? Write a paragraph to persuade readers to agree with you.

Harcourt

Name _____

Skill Reminder To decode a long word, look for a prefix, a
suffix, or a familiar word part.

▶ Read the newspaper article. Complete the chart by writing
prefix, suffix, or *familiar word part* to indicate a strategy or strategies for
figuring out each underlined word. Then write the word's meaning
from the phrases in the box.

Talented Students Entertain Crowd

The fourth-grade students from
the Cedar Park School put on an
extraordinary performance at City Park
last evening. Three girls sang together,
their voices blending in harmonious
tunes. Several students performed their
own compositions on guitar and drums.
One young man even played the
bagpipes. For more than an hour, music
resounded throughout the park.

musical instrument made of a bag and several pipes
having pleasing harmony   better than ordinary
music that is composed   echoed with sound

Word	Strategy	Meaning
1. extraordinary	_____	_____
2. harmonious	_____	_____
3. compositions	_____	_____
4. bagpipes	_____	_____
5. resounded	_____	_____

Harcourt

▶ Before you read, fill in the prediction chart by writing what you think will happen. After you read, write what actually happens.

What I Predict Will Happen	What Actually Happens

▶ Write a one-sentence summary telling how Miss Peterson gets Janey to change her negative attitude.

_____

_____

_____

Harcourt

Name _____

▶ **Read the definitions. Write the meaning of each underlined word as it is used in each sentence.**

bee: (a) a type of insect; **(b)** a gathering of people

board: (a) a thin slab of material having a certain purpose, as a chalkboard; **(b)** a group of people who direct something

pens: (a) small fenced areas for keeping animals; **(b)** instruments for writing with ink

stories: (a) tales; **(b)** floors of a building

yard: (a) a measurement of 36 inches; **(b)** the ground next to a building

1. My great-aunt went to school in a building two <u>stories</u> tall.

   _____

2. Her desk was only about a <u>yard</u> away from the teacher's desk.

   _____

3. One day a <u>bee</u> flew in through the window and caused a panic.

   _____

4. The teacher had the students read <u>stories</u> about faraway places like Borneo.

   _____

5. Ink and <u>pens</u> were not allowed, so Aunt Margaret wrote with pencil.

   _____

6. She also liked to write and draw on the <u>board</u>.

   _____

7. The school <u>board</u> placed an American flag in every classroom.

   _____

8. Aunt Margaret's class always had a spelling <u>bee</u> on Friday.

   _____

9. At recess the students played in the grassy <u>yard</u> behind the school.

   _____

10. The farmer kept the pigs in <u>pens</u>.

   _____

SCHOOL-HOME CONNECTION With your child, begin a list of words you hear or see that have more than one meaning. Keep the list in a place where both of you can add to it easily.

Touch a Dream **175**

Harcourt

Name _____

▶ **Denotation** is the exact or dictionary meaning of a word. **Connotation** is the meaning a word suggests. Read each pair of sentences. Then answer the questions that follow.

When we first moved to the farm, Pa built a small shed for us to live in. Next to our neighbor's beautiful house, it looked like a shack.

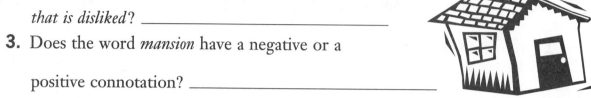

1. Which two words denote a *small building*? _____

2. Which of the two words you wrote connotes *something*

that is disliked? _____

3. Does the word *mansion* have a negative or a

positive connotation? _____

The fabric in this old dress is worn. It looks ragged compared to my other clothes.

4. Which two words denote *shabby*? _____

5. Which of the words you wrote connotes *extremely shabby*? _____

6. Does the word *elegant* have a negative or a positive connotation?

_____

This morning when I was washing dishes, I broke my mother's favorite plate. I was very upset when it shattered on the floor.

7. Which two words denote *caused to come apart*? _____

8. Which of the words you wrote connotes *into many pieces*? _____

9. Does the word *mend* have a negative or a positive

connotation? _____

My grandma was happy when she saw us drive up. She was delighted when she saw that we had brought the dog along, too.

10. Which two words denote *pleased*? _____

11. Which of the words you wrote connotes *extremely pleased*? _____

12. Does the word *miserable* have a negative or a positive connotation?

_____

Harcourt

Name _____

▶ **Write the verb from each sentence in the column where it belongs.**

1. The migrant workers picked cotton all week.

2. Later they will help with the berry crop.

3. Some of the workers arrived from up North.

4. Others stayed out West most of the year.

5. A few workers will eventually become landowners.

6. Most will return to the fields next year.

Past-Tense Verbs	Future-Tense Verbs

▶ **Complete each sentence with the correct form of the verb in parentheses ( ).**

7. We _____ in the middle of the year. (**move—past tense**)

8. In this town, school _____ very early. (**start—past tense**)

9. We _____ other migrant workers' children.
(**meet—future tense**)

10. As we get to know each other, we _____ friends.
(**become—future tense**)

TRY THIS! Think of two action verbs that end in *-ed* in the past tense. On a separate sheet of paper, use each verb in a past-tense sentence and in a future-tense sentence.

Harcourt

Name _____

▶ **Write a Spelling Word to complete each sentence.**

1. Max _____ the classroom.

2. Meanwhile, Bruce and Tia are _____ the flag outside.

3. Tran's job this week is _____ the door after the class leaves the room.

4. No one _____ about letting Tran do it.

5. Bob is _____ a funny book.

6. Look! I'm _____ the top shelf.

7. I feel shy when I'm _____ to the class.

8. Luz and I _____ first.

9. This puppy _____ to my neighbor.

10. Carlos has _____ outside.

11. We _____ the puppies carefully.

12. All the puppies are _____ us to be their friends.

SPELLING WORDS
1. stepped
2. entered
3. reaching
4. allowing
5. argued
6. speaking
7. reading
8. unfolding
9. finished
10. closing
11. hugged
12. belonged

Handwriting Tip: Take care to close the letter *d* and not to loop the up and down strokes, or it might look like *cl*. Write the Spelling Words below.

entered

13. stepped _____   15. argued _____

14. reading _____   16. hugged _____

Harcourt

Name _____

▶ **Choose words from the lamppost to complete the sentences below.**

culture   chile   barbecue   mesquite   confetti   accordion

Attention All Neighbors!

This Saturday and Sunday we will hold an outdoor

(1) _____ in our neighborhood. The purpose

is to celebrate the **(2)** _____ of the

Southwest. All kinds of food will be served, including some tacos,

and some hot, spicy **(3)** _____!

We'll supply everything from the cups and plates to the coals of

(4) _____ wood! Just bring your appetites!

A musician will play the **(5)** _____.

Sing along! Throw **(6)** _____!

Come celebrate!

▶ **Write the word from the lamppost that completes each analogy.**

7. *Tomato* is to *ketchup* as *spice* is to _____.

8. *Strum* is to *guitar* as *squeeze* is to _____.

9. *Log* is to *wood chips* as *paper* is to _____.

10. *Sandwich* is to *picnic* as *hamburger* is to _____.

SCHOOL-HOME CONNECTION With your child, talk about your favorite family meals, vacations, or traditions. Use at least two of the Vocabulary Words.

Harcourt

Name _____

▶ Complete the character map below. Include information about each character.

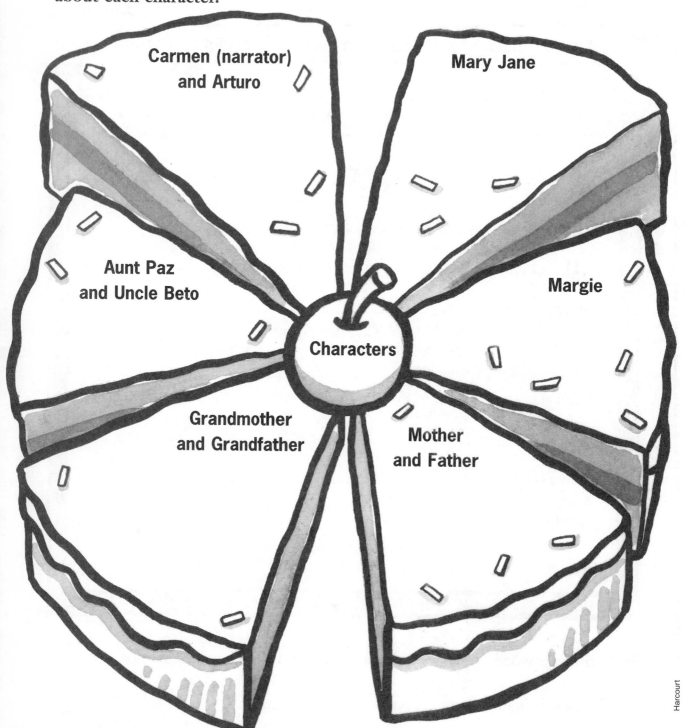

▶ How can you tell that Carmen's family is a close one?

_____

_____

Name _____

▶ **Skim the article below. Then, on the next page, answer the questions.**

At Home in a Castle

Can you imagine what it was like to live in a castle? Hundreds of years ago, rich landowners called lords built strong buildings where they and the people who lived nearby could be safe when enemies attacked. One kind of castle was called a *motte and bailey* castle. The motte was the tall mound of earth where a tower was built. The bailey was the courtyard where many smaller buildings were located.

The Bailey

For protection from enemies, the bailey was surrounded by a *moat*, a ditch filled with water. A wooden drawbridge could be lowered across the moat to let people into the bailey. Inside the moat, a fence encircled the bailey. The buildings and fences were both made of wood. Sometimes attackers burned them down.

A Community Inside

The bailey was really a small village. There was a stable for housing the animals. Barracks provided a place for the lord's soldiers to stay. A barn and storehouses held food and other supplies. There might even be a small church, a kitchen, and a bakery. Feasts were held in the great hall. The bailey could be very crowded with servants, workers, and soldiers all going about their business.

GO ON ⟹

Harcourt

Name _____

▶ Now that you have skimmed the article on the preceding page, write the answer to the questions below. Choose from the words or phrases below each line. You may turn back to scan for information when necessary.

1. From the headings, you can tell that this article is about

_____.

life in a castle   **how to be a knight**   **life on the frontier**

2. To find out what materials were used to build the bailey, the reader should

look in the section under the heading _____.
The Bailey   **A Community Inside**   **At Home in a Castle**

3. The section "A Community Inside" will probably be about

_____.

what knights ate   **how to build walls**   **activities in the castle**

4. A bailey was _____.
a tall tower   **a moat**   **a courtyard**

5. A motte and bailey castle was made of _____.
stone   **wood**   **bricks**

6. A lord was _____.
a kind of church   **a kind of castle**   **a rich landowner**

7. A moat was _____.
the great hall   **a drawbridge**   **a ditch around the bailey**

8. Soldiers stayed in the _____.
great hall   **motte**   **barracks**

9. Feasts were held in the _____.
tower   **great hall**   **storehouses**

10. The bailey was crowded with _____.
lords and ladies   **knights and bakers**   **soldiers and workers**

Harcourt

▶ **Complete the chart with the correct form of each verb.**

	Verb	Present	Past	Past with Helping Verb
1.	be	am, is, are		(have, has, had)
2.	go	go, goes		(have, has, had)
3.	think	think, thinks		(have, has, had)
4.	know	know, knows		(have, has, had)
5.	wear	wear, wears		(have, has, had)

▶ **Complete each sentence with the correct past-tense form of the verb in parentheses ( ).**

6. Grandma _____ a colorful apron. **(wear)**

7. She _____ four eggs into a bowl. **(break)**

8. Then she _____ the shells in the trash. **(throw)**

9. Outside, the day had _____. **(begin)**

10. Grandpa had _____ in the newspaper. **(bring)**

TRY THIS! Choose two verbs from the chart. Write two sentences for each verb. In the first sentence, use the past-tense form. In the second sentence, use the past with a helping verb.

Harcourt

Name _____

▶ **Write the Spelling Word that rhymes with each word below.**

1. home   _____

2. out   _____

3. ham   _____

4. hums   _____

5. missile   _____

6. strum   _____

SPELLING WORDS

1. lamb
2. often
3. castle
4. listen
5. comb
6. climbed
7. fasten
8. crumbs
9. soften
10. thumb
11. doubt
12. whistle

▶ **Unscramble the underlined letters. Write the correct Spelling Words on the lines.**

7. I <u>fento</u> think about painting.   _____

8. I mix paints to <u>tenfos</u> colors.   _____

9. I <u>staenf</u> my mind on the scene I want to paint.   _____

10. I sing while I paint, but don't let anyone <u>nestil</u>.   _____

11. My favorite painting shows the tower of an old <u>stacel</u>.   _____

12. I <u>mebcdli</u> up the tower.   _____

Handwriting Tip: Use an overcurve joining stroke in writing *m*, so that it doesn't look like *n*. Write the Spelling Words below. _____ /m

13. lamb _____   15. climbed _____

14. comb _____   16. thumb _____

SCHOOL-HOME CONNECTION With your child, use the first six Spelling Words in three sentences. Help your child use two words in each sentence.

Harcourt

Name _____

▶ **Write the word from the pots that matches each clue.**

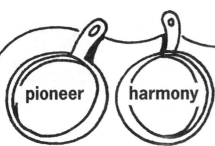

(pioneer) (harmony) (fertile) (arbor) (possibilities)

1. things that may happen _____

2. musical notes sung together _____

3. a shelter shaded by
   vines or branches _____

4. able to produce a lot _____

5. an early settler _____

▶ **Write the Vocabulary Word that answers each riddle.**

6. I sound nice in a song.
   What am I? _____

7. I traveled to live on unsettled
   land. Who am I? _____

8. With me, anything may
   happen. What am I? _____

9. I'm a shelter covered with
   vines. What am I? _____

10. My kind of soil grows many
    crops. What kind of soil am I? _____

Harcourt

 TRY THIS! Imagine that you are a pioneer on another planet. Describe what you see and hear and how you live. Use at least two Vocabulary Words.

Name _____

Skill Reminder | Use encyclopedias, dictionaries, atlases, and globes to help you find information.

▶ **Help Molly prepare a report about Oklahoma. Beside each question, write where she should look for the information she needs. Choose from the words in the box.**

| encyclopedia | dictionary | atlas | globe |

1. What states border on Oklahoma? _____

2. When did Oklahoma become a state? _____

3. How far is it from my hometown to Oklahoma City? _____

4. What crops are grown in Oklahoma? _____

5. What place is on the exact opposite side of Earth from Oklahoma? _____

6. Why is Oklahoma called "The Sooner State"? _____

7. How is the word *drought* pronounced? _____

8. Which major highways pass through Tulsa, Oklahoma? _____

9. What are some important dates in Oklahoma's history? _____

10. Does Oklahoma have any lakes and rivers? _____

 TRY THIS! Plan a report about your state. Make a list of the information you need and where you would find it.

Harcourt

Name _____

Skill Reminder **A generalization is a conclusion based on information the writer gives.**

▶ **Read this passage from a diary that Lizzie wrote about her family's experience as homesteaders. Then write** *valid* **or** *invalid* **beside each generalization.**

I'll never forget how blue and bright that Oklahoma sky was when I was a child! The first year that our family lived on our homestead in the Oklahoma Territory, it hardly rained at all. The soil felt like stone, and it was hard work to plow it and plant crops. For weeks we watched the sky, hoping for rain to water the seeds and make them grow. Those were hard times. We didn't get a crop that first year, so we had nothing to sell so we could buy supplies. It was a good thing that Mother planted a patch of vegetables. Her garden was near our well, so we were able to water it. The beans and peas and potatoes she raised were enough to keep the family fed. Our second year was much better. Father raised a good crop, and we children even got new pairs of shoes!

Generalization	Valid or Invalid
1. It never rains in Oklahoma.	_____
2. Soil becomes hard when it is very dry.	_____
3. Homesteaders had no shoes.	_____
4. Homesteaders needed rain for their crops.	_____
5. Dry years made for hard times for homesteaders.	_____
6. All homesteaders planted vegetable gardens.	_____
7. Vegetable gardens helped keep some homesteaders from being hungry.	_____
8. It is always hot in Oklahoma.	_____
9. All homesteaders were happy.	_____
10. Weather was important to homesteaders.	_____

Harcourt

Name _____

▶ Complete the cause-and-effect fishbone.

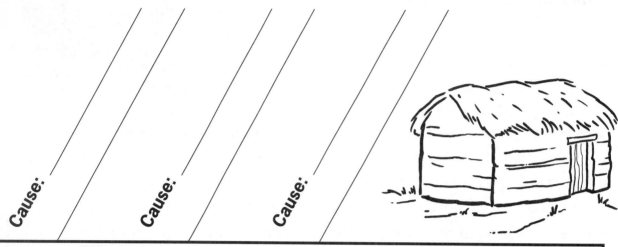

Cause:

Cause:

Cause:

Effect: The narrator claims land in the Oklahoma Territory.

Cause:

Cause:

Cause:

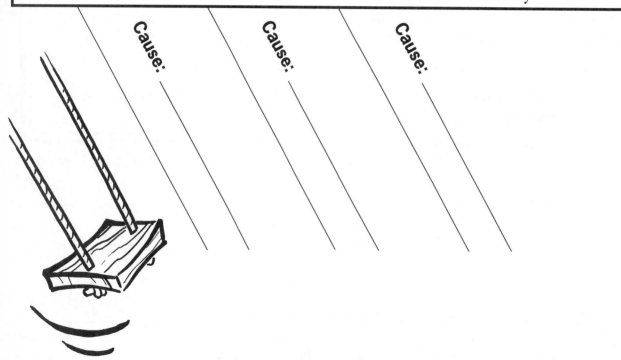

▶ Write a one-sentence summary of the whole selection.

_____

_____

_____

_____

188 Touch a Dream

Harcourt

Name _____

▶ **Read the words and their meanings. In each sentence, use
context clues to help you decide what the underlined word
means in that sentence. Then write that meaning of the word.**

	Meaning 1	Meaning 2	Meaning 3
crop:	a product grown on a farm	trim the edges	a short haircut
draft:	related to pulling heavy loads	select for a job	a current of air
raise:	grow	set up or build	an increase in pay
stable:	a building for animals	not easy to shake or move	not changing
smart:	intelligent	in style	feel a sharp sting

1. I cut my finger on the edge of one
   of the photos, and did that ever <u>smart</u>!   _____

2. I had to <u>crop</u> some of the photos
   so they would fit in my album.   _____

3. These pictures show the garden
   where we <u>raise</u> vegetables.   _____

4. This photo shows a field of corn,
   our best <u>crop</u>.   _____

5. We use horses as <u>draft</u> animals to
   pull loaded wagons.   _____

6. Our biggest horse, Jeb, helped
   <u>raise</u> the walls of our new house by
   pulling the boards into place.   _____

7. We nailed the boards together so
   our walls would be <u>stable</u> when
   strong winds blow.   _____

8. Jeb is so <u>smart</u> that he seems to
   know what to do before we tell him.   _____

Look in a dictionary and find an unfamiliar word that has more than one
meaning. Write sentences using each meaning of the word.

Harcourt

▶ **Read each sentence. Choose the answer that best tells the meaning of the underlined word as it is used in the sentence. Mark the letter of that answer.**

1 I read an exciting <u>novel</u> about pioneer life.

Ⓐ new or unusual

Ⓑ sports event

Ⓒ a long piece of fiction

Ⓓ type of farm

2 The pioneers built their houses in a <u>novel</u> way, using blocks of earth called sod.

Ⓕ new or unusual

Ⓖ brick

Ⓗ a long piece of fiction

Ⓙ modern

3 A pioneer would build a <u>shed</u> to store equipment or food.

Ⓐ to send forth

Ⓑ to cast off

Ⓒ a small, low building

Ⓓ "she would"

4 Sometimes a snowstorm would <u>strand</u> a family on the prairie for weeks.

Ⓕ a thread twisted into a rope

Ⓖ to leave helpless

Ⓗ a beach or shore

Ⓙ to run a ship onto the shore

5 Grasshoppers, weevils, and <u>flies</u> were pests on the farms.

Ⓐ kind of insect

Ⓑ runs away

Ⓒ moves quickly

Ⓓ travels through the air

6 Often a hired <u>hand</u> became more like a family member than just a helper.

Ⓕ body part at the end of the arm

Ⓖ a round of clapping

Ⓗ worker

Ⓙ a pointer on a clock

7 Trees were so rare on the plains that they were <u>points</u> of interest.

Ⓐ sharp tips

Ⓑ brings attention with a stick or a finger

Ⓒ certain places

Ⓓ a strip of land that extends into a body of water

Harcourt

Name _____

▶ **Write the word that means the same as the underlined word.**

1. I like my <u>flapjacks</u> with butter and syrup.

   Flapjacks are probably _____.
   cookies   **pancakes**   **eggrolls**

2. Mom said she would <u>fix</u> dinner.

   Fix probably means _____.
   fasten   **prepare**   **repair**

3. Our breakfast of <u>grits</u> warmed us as we ventured out in the snow.

   Grits are probably _____.
   hot cereal   **eggs**   **toast**

4. Jimmy loved to fish for <u>crawdads</u>.

   Crawdads are probably _____.
   fathers   **squirrels**   **crayfish**

5. The <u>cane</u> crop produced a lot of sugar this year.

   Cane is probably a _____.
   stick for walking   **sugar plant**   **candy**

6. We ground the <u>goobers</u> until we had peanut butter.

   Goobers are probably _____.
   leaves   **raisins**   **peanuts**

7. Mom and I sat on the front <u>stoop</u> and watched our neighbors

   walking past. *Stoop* probably means _____.
   shed   **sidewalk**   **porch**

8. Jesse bought a new <u>skillet</u> for cooking eggs.

   A *skillet* is probably _____.
   a teapot   **something to learn**   **a frying pan**

TRY THIS! Ask your family, friends, and teacher about words that are unique to where you live. Keep a running list of these regional words.

Harcourt

Name _____

▶ **Write the contraction for each word pair.**

1. she is   _____

2. have not   _____

3. would not   _____

4. is not   _____

5. I have   _____

6. he had   _____

7. it is   _____

8. do not   _____

▶ **Write the negative from each sentence.**

9. Nobody rides in covered wagons today. _____

10. Wagons were never a great way to travel. _____

▶ **Rewrite each sentence. Get rid of double negatives. Use the correct
pronoun or contraction.**

11. You never wanted to be no pioneer.

_____

12. Your sure its too hard a life?

_____

**TRY
THIS!**

Use each word pair in a sentence.
    its/it's   *their/they're*
Use each word in a sentence.
    nobody   *never*

Harcourt

Name _____

▶ **Write the contraction for each of the underlined words.**

1. Life <u>was not</u> easy for pioneers. _____

2. They <u>did not</u> have any luxuries. _____

3. <u>I would</u> miss a microwave oven. _____

4. <u>You would</u> miss canned food. _____

5. We <u>have not</u> had to chop wood. _____

6. Mom says <u>she would</u> like to
   try living the life of a pioneer. _____

7. Who <u>would not</u> like to? _____

8. <u>I have</u> read that tourists can
   take trips in covered wagons. _____

9. Now <u>we have</u> written to
   several travel agencies. _____

10. Here are the pamphlets
    <u>they have</u> sent us. _____

11. One company still
    <u>has not</u> replied. _____

12. After <u>you have</u> read
    this brochure, tell me
    what you think of it. _____

SPELLING WORDS
1. hasn't
2. I've
3. I'd
4. we've
5. wouldn't
6. you'd
7. haven't
8. wasn't
9. they've
10. you've
11. she'd
12. didn't

Handwriting Tip: When you write a
contraction, do not connect the letter before the
apostrophe to the letter after the apostrophe. Write
the Spelling Words below.

hasn't

13. hasn't _____   15. they've _____

14. haven't _____   16. she'd _____

Harcourt

▶ **Write the word below that completes each sentence.**

bellowing   softhearted   ration   tragedy   fateful   gadgets

Many tall tales tell of legendary characters who are big both in
size and in deeds. Somehow though, we tend to think of giants as
unpleasant. Remember the giant in "Jack and the Beanstalk"? Was he

kind and **(1)** _____, or was he scary? If the giant
had plenty of food, do you think he would share it freely with others

or **(2)** _____ it in very small amounts?
Can you imagine what it would sound like to hear the giant

(3) _____ for his pet? Can you picture the size of

his household **(4)** _____, such as his can opener or

nutcracker? It is a **(5)** _____ that because of one
mean giant, other giants are thought of in the same way. Paul Bunyan

was kind and **(6)** _____. You would never hear him

(7) _____ at his pet ox unless he thought Babe was

lost. He was the best logger ever. It was a **(8)** _____
day when Paul Bunyan decided to stop working.

▶ **Write the Vocabulary Word that means the *opposite* of each word below.**

9. comedy   _____

10. strict   _____

11. whispering _____

TRY THIS! Make up your own story about something unusual that Paul Bunyan and
Babe did. Use at least two Vocabulary Words.

Harcourt

Name _____

Skill Reminder Some words have more than one meaning. Use context clues to help you figure out the word's meaning in the sentence.

▶ Write the meaning that each underlined word has. Choose from the meanings in the box.

bit: (a) a tiny amount; **(b)** the metal part of a bridle that fits in a horse's mouth
bored: (a) made weary by being dull; **(b)** made a hole through
bright: (a) clever; **(b)** glowing with color or light
plain: (a) not decorated or fancy; **(b)** a level area of land
sport: (a) a game or contest; **(b)** to wear or display
stir: (a) excitement or great interest; **(b)** to move around with a circular motion
yarn: (a) a story; **(b)** a type of string used in knitting and weaving

1. Did you ever hear the <u>yarn</u> about how the forest got its color?

_____

2. Long ago, everything in the forest was <u>plain</u> black and white and gray, just

like in an old movie. _____

3. Jiggs Jiggerson, who was a <u>bright</u> young lad, put his brain to work on the

problem. _____

4. First he <u>bored</u> a hole in the sky and drained out some blue.

_____

5. Then Jiggs sliced off a <u>bit</u> of yellow from the sun. _____

6. He began to <u>stir</u> the blue and yellow together, and got green.

_____

7. Jiggs got to work with his paintbrush, and soon every tree in the forest could

<u>sport</u> pretty green leaves. _____

TRY THIS!   Use some underlined words on this page to write your own tall tale.

Harcourt

Name _____

▶ Before you read the story and as you read, fill in the
prediction chart by writing what you think will happen.
After you read, write what actually happens.

What I Predict Will Happen

What Actually Happens

▶ Write a one-sentence summary describing what Paul relies on Babe for
through the years.

_____

_____

Harcourt

Name _____

▶ **Read the story beginning. Then write *yes* or *no* after each
statement to indicate whether a reader could correctly
make that inference.**

I was standing in my cabin, looking out the window at the beautiful stack of
firewood I'd just finished chopping, when I saw something that made my hair
stand on end. "Jackie! Frankie! Tess!" I yelled to my kids. "Will you
look at that!" The kids came running to the window and looked out.

"Bees, Papa!" cried Tess.

"The biggest bees I ever saw!" shouted Jackie.

"Yes," I cried, "and they're trying to build a hive in my pile of
firewood!" Quick as a wink, we ran outside, yelling, "Scram, you bees!"
One bee had already picked up my ax and was trying to chop a hole in
a big log for a doorway. You won't believe what happened next.

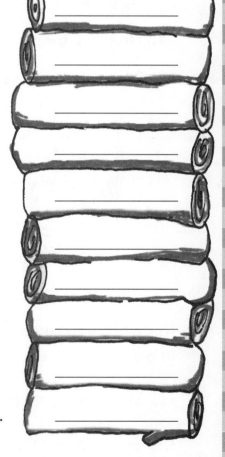

1. This is a true story. _____

2. The person telling the story is a father. _____

3. An ax is a tool for chopping firewood. _____

4. The storyteller is proud of his stack of firewood. _____

5. Only four people live in the cabin. _____

6. The storyteller has at least three children. _____

7. The storyteller burns wood. _____

8. The children can chop firewood. _____

9. The storyteller was very surprised by the bees. _____

10. The storyteller doesn't want bees in his firewood. _____

TRY THIS! Reread a passage from one of your favorite stories. Make a list of the
inferences you can make from the passage.

Harcourt

Name _____

▶ **Underline the verb. Circle the adverb that describes it.
Then tell whether the adverb tells** *where,* *when,* **or** *how.*

1. The huge ox rushed over.   _____

2. He quickly drank the whole lake.   _____

3. The loggers shouted angrily.   _____

4. They never saw such a thirsty beast.   _____

5. A thousand fish flopped nearby.   _____

6. Now Babe felt content.   _____

7. He lay down with a grunt.   _____

8. Later, the loggers heard a roar.   _____

9. Dropping their axes, they ran fast.   _____

10. The blue ox snored peacefully.   _____

▶ **Rewrite each sentence. Add an adverb that gives the information
in parentheses ( ).**

11. Babe took a nap. **(when)** _____

12. The loggers rested. **(where)** _____

SCHOOL–HOME CONNECTION Look at some family photographs
with your child. Then have your child write captions for several of the
photographs, using an adverb in each caption. Here are some examples:
Grandma smiles happily.   *Aunt Sara always brings pie.*

Harcourt

▶ **Write two Spelling Words to complete each sentence. Use a pair of homophones in each sentence.**

1.–2. I'll give you _____ numbers to add,

and you can tell us the _____.

3.–4. Do you want to hear the _____ of

a bear with a long, bushy _____?

5.–6. As we stood on the _____, we saw

two _____ flying overhead.

7.–8. The wind _____ so hard that our

_____ tent nearly collapsed.

9.–10. Please _____ the door to the

_____ closet.

11.–12. Clearly, we'll have no _____

until we give the dog a _____
of our meat.

SPELLING WORDS
1. some
2. sum
3. tale
4. plains
5. close
6. blew
7. piece
8. clothes
9. tail
10. planes
11. blue
12. peace

Handwriting Tip: Make sure the letter *l* touches the top
writing line. Otherwise, it might look like an *e*. Write the
Spelling Words below.

13. plains _____   **15.** planes _____

14. blew _____   **16.** blue _____

Harcourt

▶ **Write the word from the boat that matches each clue. Some words will be used twice. The message in the oar tells you what nationality TJ's mother is.**

| hysterically | overwhelm | interpreter | appetizing |
| equivalent | irrigation | occasionally | |

1. equal   _ _ _ _ _ _ _ _ _ _

2. sometimes   _ _ _ _ _ _ _ _ _ _ _

3. overpower   _ _ _ _ _ _ _ _ _

4. system for watering   _ _ _ _ _ _ _ _ _ _

5. translator   _ _ _ _ _ _ _ _ _ _ _

6. very tasty   _ _ _ _ _ _ _ _ _ _

7. rush at and crush   _ _ _ _ _ _ _ _ _

8. with wild emotion   _ _ _ _ _ _ _ _ _ _ _

9. once in a while   _ _ _ _ _ _ _ _ _ _ _ _

10. the same as   _ _ _ _ _ _ _ _ _ _

SCHOOL-HOME CONNECTION With your child, talk about the countries your family's relatives and ancestors came from. Tell about the trips those people made to come to the United States. Use at least three Vocabulary Words.

Harcourt

Name _____

Skill Reminder Use context clues to help you figure out what an unfamiliar word means.

▶ Read the sentences. Use context clues to help you figure out what each underlined word means. Then write each underlined word beside its meaning listed below.

The eel is not a snake, but it is so long and <u>slender</u> that it looks a little like one. <u>Naturalists</u> study eels to learn more about their life cycle.

Crocodiles like warm weather, so they live in <u>tropical</u> areas. They <u>inhabit</u> places where there is shallow water. Crocodiles are <u>aggressive</u> animals and may attack large animals or people. Be careful not to <u>agitate</u> a crocodile!

Some water buffalo are no longer wild animals and have been <u>domesticated</u> for use as farm animals. They are <u>brawny</u> animals and can pull a plow in deep mud. In fact, they <u>revel</u> in wallowing in mud! The milk of the water buffalo is healthful and <u>nourishing</u>.

1. quick to attack   _____

2. to enjoy very much   _____

3. thin   _____

4. to live in a place   _____

5. describing something that keeps someone healthy   _____

6. scientists who study nature   _____

7. strong   _____

8. to disturb or excite   _____

9. tamed   _____

10. located in the hot, wet part of the Earth near the equator   _____

SCHOOL-HOME CONNECTION With your child, find a magazine article. Help your child use context clues to find the meanings of unfamiliar words.

Harcourt

Name _____

▶ Fill in the first two columns of the K-W-L chart. Then use
information from the story to fill in the last column.

K	W	L
What I <u>K</u>now	What I <u>W</u>ant to Know	What I <u>L</u>earned

▶ Think about all the things TJ experiences in Vietnam. List five ways that
life in Vietnam is different from life in America.

1. _____

2. _____

3. _____

4. _____

5. _____

Harcourt

Name _____

▶ **Study the map, graph, and diagram. Then answer the questions about each.**

Colorado

Population of Vietnam

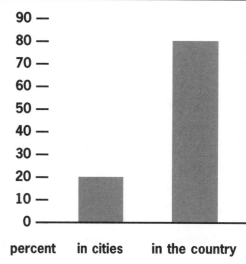

1. In which direction would you travel to go from Denver to Colorado Springs?

_____

2. What mountain range is found in Colorado?

_____

3. What percentage of Vietnam's people live in cities?

_____

4. What percentage of Vietnam's people live in the country?

_____

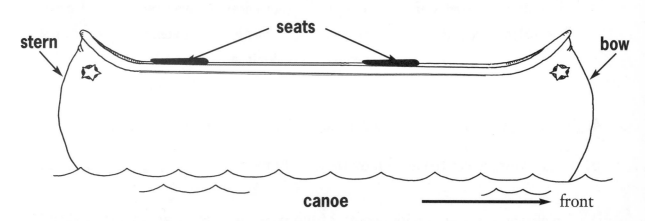

5. What is the front part of the canoe called? _____

Harcourt

Name _____

▶ **Study the table and time line. Then answer the questions.**

	Vietnam	**United States**
Farm Products	rice, cassava, sweet potatoes, sugarcane, coffee, cotton	corn, wheat, cotton, soybeans, etc.
Languages	Vietnamese, Chinese, English, Khmer	English, Spanish, etc.
Capital	Hanoi	Washington, D.C.
Population	about 74,000,000	about 266,000,000

1. Does Vietnam or the United States have a

larger population? _____

2. Which farm product is grown in both countries? _____

3. Which language is spoken in both countries? _____

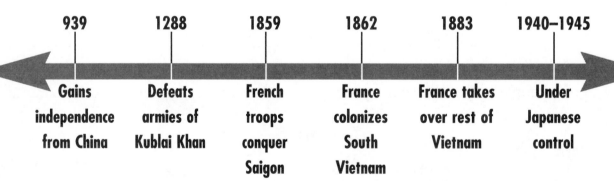

939	1288	1859	1862	1883	1940–1945
Gains independence from China	Defeats armies of Kublai Khan	French troops conquer Saigon	France colonizes South Vietnam	France takes over rest of Vietnam	Under Japanese control

4. In what year did Vietnam gain independence from China? _____

5. What country controlled Vietnam after France? _____

TRY THIS! Think about some school events of the past year, such as special activities and celebrations. Make a time line to show these important events.

Harcourt

Name _____

▶ **Study the table and graph. Then choose the answer that best completes each sentence, and mark the letter of that answer.**

Type of Animal in Vietnam	Examples
Large Mammals	elephants, deer, bears, tigers, leopards
Smaller Mammals	monkeys, squirrels, otters
Reptiles	crocodiles, snakes, lizards

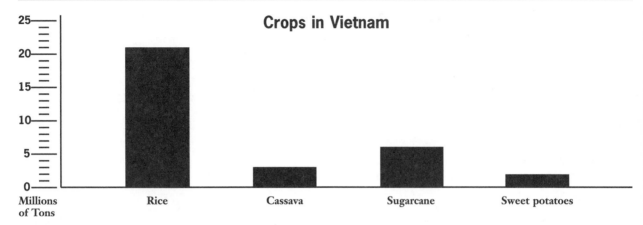

Crops in Vietnam

Millions of Tons — Rice, Cassava, Sugarcane, Sweet potatoes

1 A reptile *not* found in Vietnam is the
_____.

A crocodile

B alligator

C snake

D lizard

2 Vietnam's largest main crop is _____.

F rice

G cassava

H sugarcane

J sweet potatoes

3 Vietnam grew 6 million tons of
_____.

A rice

B cassava

C sugarcane

D sweet potatoes

4 A map would be best for showing
_____.

F highways and rivers

G dates when different rulers were in power

H amounts of rainfall in different years

J the parts of a plow

5 The best graphic source for showing the design of a helicopter is a _____.

A map

B time line

C graph

D diagram

Answers
1 Ⓐ Ⓑ Ⓒ Ⓓ
2 Ⓕ Ⓖ Ⓗ Ⓙ
3 Ⓐ Ⓑ Ⓒ Ⓓ
4 Ⓕ Ⓖ Ⓗ Ⓙ
5 Ⓐ Ⓑ Ⓒ Ⓓ

Harcourt

Name _____

▶ **Rewrite each sentence, using the correct form of the
adverb in parentheses ( ).**

1. Does rice grow **(taller, tallest)** than corn? _____

   _____

2. The ox pulls the **(harder, hardest)** of all the beasts of burden. _____

   _____

3. A buffalo plows **(more quickly, most quickly)** than a cow. _____

   _____

4. The tail of the ox wags **(more jerkily, most jerkily)** of all. _____

   _____

5. Do oxen live **(longer, longest)** than buffalo do? _____

   _____

▶ **Complete each sentence with the correct
form of the adverb in parentheses ( ).**

6. The van bumped _____
   than a covered wagon. **(wildly)**

7. It traveled the _____
   of all the vehicles on the road. **(fast)**

8. The road itself wound _____
   than the clouds. **(high)**

9. Road crews worked _____
   in winter than during the monsoon season. **(frequently)**

10. Of all the road's obstacles, the potholes slowed us

    _____. **(forcefully)**

Harcourt

Name _____

▶ **Write the Spelling Word that matches each clue.**

1. They've all joined a group. _____

2. It's the opposite of *deep*. _____

3. It "makes perfect." _____

4. It's an evening meal. _____

5. Use this word instead of
   imagine. _____

6. It may be difficult, but you
   can solve it. _____

7. Part of this plant is used to
   make clothes. _____

8. If you refuse to change
   your mind, people may
   call you this. _____

9. It is another word for *thing*. _____

10. It's a shiny metal. _____

11. It can protect you from
    bad weather or danger. _____

12. When you leave something
    out, you often use this word. _____

SPELLING WORDS
1. practice
2. members
3. dinner
4. suppose
5. except
6. problem
7. shallow
8. stubborn
9. silver
10. cotton
11. object
12. shelter

Handwriting Tip: Leave enough space between
double letters so they will be easy to read. Write the
Spelling Words below.

13. suppose _____   15. cotton _____

14. stubborn _____   16. shallow _____

SCHOOL-HOME CONNECTION With your child, think of
other words that have double letters. Then find words that
they rhyme with.

Touch a Dream **207**

Harcourt

Name _____

▶ **Write the word from the box that best goes with each pair.**
One word will be used twice.

carnivorous	boggiest	chemicals	dissolve
accidentally	fertilizer	victim	

1. melt
liquid

_____

2. grow
plants

_____

3. meat-eating
hungry

_____

4. unintentionally
unplanned

_____

5. swampy
thickest

_____

6. not on purpose
unexpectedly

_____

7. injured
harmed

_____

8. scientist
substances

_____

▶ **Write the Vocabulary Word from the box above that**
means the *opposite* of each term below.

9. vegetable-eating _____

10. freeze _____

11. attacker _____

12. intentionally _____

TRY THIS! Imagine that you are a plant or an animal. Write sentences that tell what you do to survive the dangers where you live. Use some Vocabulary Words.

Harcourt

Name _____

Skill Reminder Use graphs, maps, time lines, tables, and diagrams to help you find information quickly.

▶ Five students planted seeds in flowerpots. Use the graph to see how many of each student's seeds sprouted. Then answer the questions.

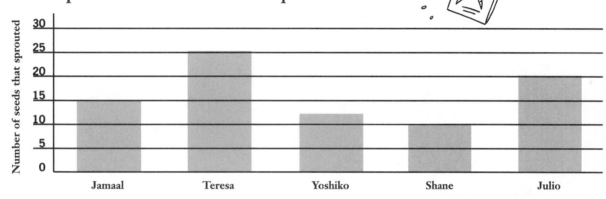

1. Which student has about 12 seeds that sprouted? _____

2. Which student has more sprouted seeds than Julio? _____

3. How many more of Teresa's seeds sprouted than Shane's? _____

4. If Julio and Jamaal put their sprouted seeds together, how many would

   they have? _____

5. If Yoshiko gave five of her sprouted seeds to Shane, how many would

   Shane have? _____

6. If Teresa gave three of her sprouted seeds to each of the other students,

   which student would have the most? _____

7. Would you use a map or a time line to show where different wildflowers

   grow in your state? _____

8. Would you use a table or a diagram to show the names of different parts of

   a sunflower? _____

TRY THIS! Make a graph to show how many desks, tables, chalkboards, computers, or other items are in your classroom.

Name _____

▶ Before you read, complete the second column of the SQ3R chart. Complete the third column during and after reading.

Survey (page, description)	Question	Read, Recite, Review (answer)
page 600 Caption that starts, "There are over 200 different kinds of bladderworts."		
page 603 Paragraph that ends, "I sent away for some sun-dew seeds of my own."		
page 605 Paragraph that starts, "I gave up on sundews after that, but I did grow a Venus flytrap."		
page 608 Paragraph that starts, "The next plant I got was a cobra lily."		
page 609 Paragraph that starts, "So I went—all the way to Malaysia."		

▶ Write a one-sentence summary of the whole selection.

_____

_____

Harcourt

Name _____

▶ **Read Marcus's report on strange plants. Then write each underlined word in the group where it belongs.**

Everybody knows that some animals can do tricks, but there are many plants that do surprising things, too. For one thing, not all plants grow in the ground. <u>Molds</u> live on other plants or even on bread or cheese. <u>Moss</u> can live on a rock or a tree. <u>Lichen</u> grows on rocks, too. <u>Ivy</u> is a plant that can climb up a tree or a wall. <u>Honeysuckle</u> and <u>grapevines</u> also climb. Did you know that there are even plants that look like other things? <u>Stone plants</u> are brown and look like desert rocks. The <u>cushion plant</u> of New Zealand looks like a white wool pillow. The <u>traveler's palm</u> tree looks like a peacock's fanned-out tail, and the <u>rain tree</u> looks like a huge umbrella!

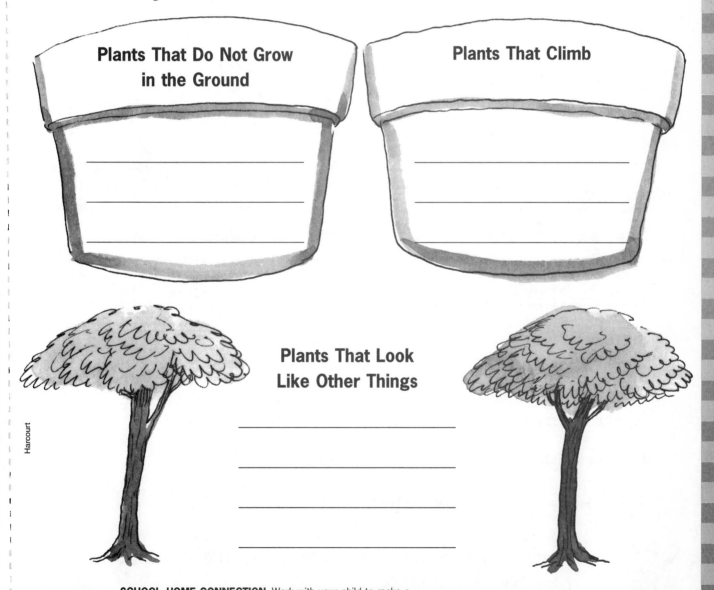

Plants That Do Not Grow in the Ground

_____

_____

_____

Plants That Climb

_____

_____

Plants That Look Like Other Things

_____

_____

_____

_____

Harcourt

SCHOOL-HOME CONNECTION Work with your child to make a list of fun things to do. Then ask your child to sort the suggestions in different ways, such as "Things to Do Indoors" and "Things to Do Outdoors" or "Things to Do Alone" and "Things to Do Together."

▶ **Underline the preposition. Circle the object of the
preposition.**

1. The flytrap grew tall in its tiny pot.

2. It leaned into the sunshine.

3. For a while, it rested quietly.

4. A small fly buzzed over the plant.

5. After a few minutes, the trap snapped.

6. The buzzing of the small insect stopped.

▶ **Use a preposition from the box to complete each
sentence. Use each word only once. Use capital
letters when necessary.**

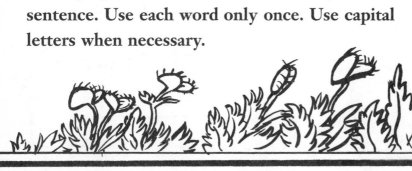

across	with	from	into	before	of

7. _____ noon, the flytrap ate seven bugs.

8. They fell _____ its trap and dissolved.

9. The leaves were armed _____ trigger hairs.

10. The tiniest insects were safe _____ the trap.

11. They walked _____ the hairs safely.

12. Many _____ the flytraps' habitats have been destroyed.

**TRY
THIS!** Choose three of the prepositions from the box above. Use each of them in
a separate sentence about plants.

Harcourt

Name _____

▶ **Unscramble the underlined words. Write the correct Spelling Words on the lines.**

1. We want to <u>olecat</u> unusual plants. _____

2. Venus flytraps are <u>tivena</u> to marshy areas in the southeast. _____

3. Other <u>jamro</u> kinds of animal-eating plants live in distant lands. _____

4. A <u>topli</u> will fly us there. _____

5. What is my <u>tomvie</u>? _____

6. I'm just interested in watching a still, <u>lentsi</u> plant catch an insect. _____

7. I hope that someday I'll see that <u>pruse</u> carnivorous plant, the Rajah pitcher plant. _____

8. I like <u>dacre</u> trees. _____

▶ **Write the Spelling Word that names each picture.**

9. _____   11. _____

10. _____   12. _____

Handwriting Tip: Do not make a loop when writing the letter *t*. Cross the *t* clearly, so that it doesn't look like an *l*. Write the Spelling Words below.

motive

13. pilot _____   14. native _____

Harcourt

Name _____

▶ **Write words from the box to complete the sentences.**

transformed	investigate	enthusiastically
decor	apparently	corridor

Dear Cousin,

You've got to see the **(1)** _____ in our

classroom. A lot of my friends and I **(2)** _____

the room into a tropical rain forest! It looks so cool! You don't suspect

anything when you're outside in the **(3)** _____.

But when you walk into the room, wow! I've never written so

(4) _____ about any class project before!

You should visit our school and **(5)** _____ for

yourself! The city newspaper is **(6)** _____

going to have a story about it. Watch for my picture!

Your cousin,

Aldo

▶ **Write the word from the box above that means the same as each word below.**

7. energetically _____

8. research _____

9. seemingly _____

10. changed _____

TRY THIS! Think of a way you'd like to decorate your classroom or a room at home. Write sentences that describe your decorations, using at least three Vocabulary Words.

Harcourt

Name _____

Skill Reminder Make inferences by putting together information from the text and your own knowledge and experience.

▶ **Read the ad. Then write _yes_ or _no_ to indicate whether a reader could correctly make that inference.**

Jungle Outfitters

We lead the safest, most exciting trips into the Amazon rain forest!

- Experienced guides.
- Paramedic or doctor accompanies each group.
- Travel by canoe and by foot deep into the rain forest.
- Price includes transportation and all meals for three weeks.
- Departures every six weeks.

Plan to bring cool, loose-fitting clothing, strong hiking boots, a canteen for drinking water, and a sleeping bag. You'll also need insect repellent and mosquito netting. Call today! 302-555-1000

1. It's hot in the rain forest. _____

2. The trip will last about three weeks. _____

3. People never get sick or hurt on the trip. _____

4. The travelers will be doing a lot of hiking. _____

5. The travelers will sleep in hotels every night. _____

6. Mosquitoes could be a problem in the rain forest. _____

7. There are no rivers in the rain forest. _____

8. Everybody loves to visit the rain forest. _____

9. Travelers in the rain forest are expected to find their own way around. _____

10. The travelers can probably leave heavy coats at home. _____

SCHOOL-HOME CONNECTION With your child, read some newspaper advertisements. Then discuss what inferences can and cannot be made.

Touch a Dream **215**

Harcourt

Name _____

▶ Complete the story map below.

Main Characters	Setting

Problem

Important Events

Solution

▶ How is the school's rain forest like a real one?

_____

_____

Name _____

▶ **Read each sentence. Then write your answer to each
statement about the underlined word.**

1. Kayla's uncle has several parrots that <u>he</u> trains for movies and
   television shows.

   He is _____.

2. Some parrots could already speak before her
   uncle got them, but he has taught <u>them</u> to
   say much more.

   Them refers to _____.

3. Some of the birds talk a lot. <u>Others</u> can do funny tricks.

   Others means _____.

4. Kayla laughed when she saw <u>one</u> lying on the floor of its cage and saying,
   "Sleepy bird!"

   One means _____.

5. Several of the birds have been in movies. Kayla's favorite parrot, Joko, did

   <u>this</u>, too. *This* is what Joko has done. He has _____.

6. In <u>one</u>, he played the part of a wild parrot.

   One means _____.

7. <u>He</u> even got to perch on a monkey's head!

   He is _____.

8. Many parrots can learn to do tricks. Joko
   learned <u>some</u> very quickly.

   Some means _____.

9. A <u>few</u> are especially good actors.

   Few refers to a few _____.

10. <u>They</u> seem to love the camera.

    They are _____.

Harcourt

Name _____

The Down
and Up Fall

Extending
Vocabulary:
Connotation/
Denotation

▶ **Write a word from the box that has a similar denotation (dictionary or exact meaning) but a different connotation (suggested meaning) than the underlined word or words.**

wolfing	stink	trampled	squeezed	deserted
show off	spattered	starving	peeked	sprinkle

1. First, Andy's dog <u>stepped on</u> my grandmother's flowers. _____

2. The burning hot dogs created quite a <u>smell</u>. _____

3. By the time lunch was finally ready, we were all <u>hungry</u>. _____

4. We all laughed at Buzzy, who was <u>gulping</u> down his food. _____

5. My little cousin Alice started to <u>perform</u>. _____

6. John and I <u>looked</u> at a little bird's nest. _____

7. We had just finished eating when it began to <u>rain</u>. _____

8. All the leftover food was <u>covered</u> with rain. _____

9. Everyone <u>got</u> under the picnic table. _____

10. By the time the rain stopped, the park was <u>empty</u>. _____

Harcourt

Name _____

▶ **Underline the prepositional phrase. Circle the preposition.**

1. Rubber plants grew in the rain forest.

2. Lucette perched on a high branch.

3. After a few minutes, she began talking.

4. She squawked at the people below.

5. A green snake with black markings appeared.

6. We almost fell into the pond.

7. We asked for a volunteer to lead us.

8. Our leader went ahead of us, and we
   formed a line.

▶ **Complete each sentence with a prepositional phrase.**

9. Bolivia brought her parrot _____.

10. _____, Lucette seemed content.

11. She preened her feathers _____.

12. She climbed _____ very carefully.

13. The students _____ clapped.

14. The green parrot then swooped _____.

15. _____ some students left.

16. Then Bolivia _____.

TRY THIS! Rewrite this sentence three times: *The students saw a parrot.*
Add a different prepositional phrase each time. How does the sentence's
meaning change?

Harcourt

Name _____

▶ **Find and circle the twelve misspelled words. Then write the words correctly on the lines.**

We've worked on difrent science projects. I can rimember each one.

Begining in the fall, we studied the solar system. Each planet had to spin in the right derection. Getting all the planets going at the same time was probly the most diffecult part of our project. The models took a lot of time and enrgy and our results were excellant.

Everyone had to descover and share importent facts about life in the rain forest.

We're about to start working on annother science project. I can't imagin what it will be!

SPELLING WORDS

1. difficult
2. probably
3. beginning
4. direction
5. discover
6. excellent
7. important
8. imagine
9. energy
10. remember
11. different
12. another

1. _____   7. _____

2. _____   8. _____

3. _____   9. _____

4. _____   10. _____

5. _____   11. _____

6. _____   12. _____

Handwriting Tip: Practice writing words you have problems with. Write the Spelling Words below.

important

13. difficult _____   **14.** beginning _____

SCHOOL-HOME CONNECTION With your child, write as many three syllable words that you can. Try to organize the words into groups, such as *ends with -tion (vacation).*